The Australian

Owner Builders Manual

Pinedale Press

Author's Notes & Instructions

This manual has been published to enable the Owner Builder to carry out the construction of his home in a more tradesman-like manner. It is also a ready reference guide for Tradesmen and Apprentices.

The illustrations will provide a visual understanding of those areas of construction that are difficult to comprehend when seen only as an elevation or plan view on the house plan.

Whilst many Owner Builders are in fact Carpenters, recommendations have been prepared on Page 6 especially for the experienced or those in the allied building trades. Also for this group it is advisable to engage a Carpenter to work alongside or have a Building Advisor regularly visit the site. The added cost will more than compensate in dollars saved on time and materials.

It is a tendency of Owner Builders to allow actual costs to exceed the original estimates resulting in having to live in an incompleted house. Be thorough in obtaining quotes and if uncertain, obtain further advice. Follow Pages 17-20 for estimating and earmark a further $2-3,000 as a 'safety margin'.

Methods and hints used in the text and illustrations are all acceptable trade practices. The contents are regularly updated.

This manual is intended as a general guide only to 'House Building Methods' and specific dimensions, specifications and design of structural members must be obtained from individually prepared plans and specifications.

Roof Framing
Because of the inherent trade experience required to construct the conventional 'cut on site' roof: the time factor, and the ease with which prefabricated truss roofs can be obtained, only the latter has been considered in this manual.

How to Use the Manual
The Owner Builder should undertake an overview reading of the manual, marking those pages which apply to the type of construction which he is proposing to adopt. During construction, reread those marked sections one or two stages ahead of the one currently under construction.

The paragraphs on 'Steps and Stages of Construction' will be an invaluable reminder of when to order materials and engage Tradesmen.

One Stage at a Time
No attempt has been made to minimise the work involved in the building or supervision of your own home. However, rather than seeing the project as one gigantic undertaking, view it as a series of small bite-sized jobs linked together.

Divide the Project into 5 Major Stages
1. Foundations & Footings
2. Floor
3. Walls
4. Roof
5. Linings and finishings
Then carry out each stage one day at a time, one job at a time.

Soil Testing
Enormous future structural problems can result if footings are not designed to suit each particular building site. Variations in subsoils can occur even between adjoining sites. With respect to the large cash outlay invested in a home, subsoil tests should be carried out by an Engineer.

Wind Categories
The dimensions of framing members are determined by the wind loads or pressures that may be imposed upon the house in the chosen locality. These wind pressures range between 28 M/S in sheltered non-cyclonic areas through to 65 M/S in exposed cyclonic areas (33 metres per second is approx. 74MPH). To determine the wind category for a particular site, enquire at the Local Building Inspectors office.

Manufacturer's Specifications
The term 'Manufacturer's Specifications' when used in this manual or as part of a notation on house plans refers to specification pamphlets obtainable free of charge from the supplier of the goods.

Companion to this Title
'How to be a Successful Owner Builder & Renovator' is the cross referenced companion to this title. It gives a birdseye view of house construction with large scale drawings on double page spreads.

It also covers in depth, brick masonry and concrete construction methods as well as sharing many 'inside the trade' tips on job management.

'Australian Owner Builder Manuals' published since the 5th edition have been cross referenced with 'How to Be a Successful Owner Builder & Renovator'. This is indicated by the letters 'HSOB' in the text.

Other Books by the Same Author:
Take Me Back to the Eighties
  (A Pen and Ink Sketch Book of 19th
  Century Australian Homes & Buildings)
The New Zealand Owner Builders Manual
How to be a Successful Owner Builder &
  Renovator
The Australian Renovators Manual
The Australian Roof Building Manual
  (Hiddle & Staines)
Australian House Building the Easy Hebel Way
The Australian Decks & Pergolas Construction
  Manual

Published by Pinedale Press

National Library of Australia
Cataloguing-in-publication data

Staines, Allan 1942
National Library of Australia card number and
ISBN number 0 9593024 1 7

Holder of Copyright
Pinedale Press
2 Lethbridge Court
CALOUNDRA QLD 4551
AUSTRALIA
For Orders, please fax (074) 919 219

Ist Edition	March	1984
Second Edition	June	1984
Reprint	August	1984
Reprint	November	1984
Third Edition	April	1985
Fourth Edition	June	1985
Reprint	September	1985
Fifth Edition	October	1986
Reprint	May	1987
Reprint	March	1988
Reprint	August	1988
Reprint	January	1989
Sixth Edition	December	1989
Reprint	September	1991
Seventh Edition	March	1993
Reprint	November	1993
Eighth Edition	September	1994
Reprint	March	1996

Australian Owner Builder Regulations

State by State Requirements

The rulings vary slightly from State to State and from time to time are modified and adjusted. It is advisable to ask your Local Builders Registration or Licensing Office of the current situation and for further details.

An Owner Builders Permit does not allow you to carry out electrical, plumbing, gas fitting or drainage.

New South Wales

Any building work including labour and material which exceeds $3,000 and which requires Council approval requires an Owner Builder to obtain (for a fee) an Owner Builders Permit from the Building Services Corporation. This applies to persons wishing to carry out all or part of the work or persons intending to only supervise licensed sub-contractors who will carry out the work.

The following regulations apply:

A. You must own or have a share in the ownership of the land upon which the building work is to be carried out and show proof.

B. You must reside in or intend to reside in the completed building yourself.

C. You can only build, alter or add onto a single dwelling or a dual occupancy (that is a two unit dwelling where each unit is a separate dwelling) which has been approved by Council.

Some Local Councils require a sign with the Owner Builder Permit Number displayed on the site. Others don't require it at all. Check with your Local Council. An Owner Builder must effect an insurance under the Act which will cover any subsequent purchaser against major structural defects if the property is sold within seven years of the issue of the permit. Request comprehensive details from the Building Services Corporation — (02) 959 1444 or 008 451 258.

Victoria

To obtain a Building Permit, the Owner Builder must register with the Housing Guarantee Fund Ltd (HGF). Should the Owner Builder wish to sell the house within seven years, an Inspection Report must be obtained from a body approved by the Office of Fair Trading and be forwarded to both the prospective buyer and the HGF. The HGF will require a fee which will then provide a guarantee to the purchaser for the remainder of the seven year period. Existing defects identified in the report will not be covered by the guarantee. Owner Builders may not build more than one dwelling every three years or more than two dwellings on the two lot subdivision every three years. Further details should be obtained from the HGF including those referring to Renovations — (03) 660 6111.

Queensland

The proposed Owner Builder must apply to Qld Building Services Authority for an Owner Builders Permit and the appropriate form must be completed. The Owner Builder must exhibit a sign on the site conforming to the regulation and showing the Permit No. The owner built house does not have the six years warranty which is available to registered Builders.

In the event of selling within the first six years, the prospective buyer must be given a notice that the house, extensions or whatever was built under an Owner

How to Sell the Owner Built House
For overcoming any selling problems associated with the owner built house, see HSOB Page 4.

Builder Permit by the person named and states that the house is not covered by insurance under the QBSA Act 1991.

The Registrar of Titles must enter a notification of the existence of Owner Builder Construction in a file attached to the titles registrar. Owner Builders proposing to build work valued over $10,000 must undertake a training course approved by the Authority. Some TAFE Colleges operate these courses. For full details contact the QBSA on 07 391 1139.

Western Australia (only applicable within the area of the Board's jurisdiction)

The Owner Builder can only build a dwelling or duplex and must obtain a licence for all building work exceeding $10,000 in value. Application for an Owner Builders Licence is made to the Local Authority. The applicant must not have obtained a licence within the previous six years and may not sell the house for three years from the date of issue of the licence without the Minister's approval. The Owner Builder is responsible for all building work and for structural soundness for a period of six years after completion. For further details contact the Builders Registration Board on (09) 321 6891.

Australian Capital Territory

Owner Builders must apply to the A.C.T. Building Control, Dept of the Environment, Land & Planning for a permit to build or extend their own home. The Owner Builder will be issued with a permit only twice in every five years in respect of a total of two blocks of land. For comprehensive information regarding issuing of Owner Builders permits, refer to the A.C.T. Dept of the Environment, Land & Planning - Building Control Office on (06) 207 6400.

South Australia

In South Australia, Owner Builders are not required to be registered or licensed to build their own home. However all sub-contractors who perform work for Owner Builders require a licence and when the value of the work exceeds $5,000 the Owner Builder must take out Indemnity Insurance. Enquire at Builders Licensing at Commercial Tribunal on (08) 226 8210 for further information.

Northern Territory

There is currently no requirement for Owner Builders Registration or licence in the Northern Territory. However, the Owner Builder is required to contribute to the Home Building Certification Fund. For further information, phone 089-897 072.

Tasmania

Registration of Building Contractors or Owner Builders wishing to construct their own home in Tasmania is not a requirement.

Owner Builders are covered by the Housing Indemnity Act for a period of six years. An owner built house can't be sold unless covered by the warranty.

Contents

Getting Started

Owner Builder's Programme
(See also IISOB Pages 5,6,7)

The 'On-site' Owner Builder

This type of Owner Builder enjoys the greatest cost saving. He carries out those tasks he feels capable of handling himself and employs skilled labour to assist with the rest. Sometimes it is advisable to employ tradesmen to erect the framing ready for lining and then complete the remaining work oneself with assistance where necessary. Some Owner Builders feel capable in the carpentry field. If so, then capitalise on cost saving by carrying out as much carpentry work as you feel capable of.

Alternatively, employ a Carpenter and become his 'hammer hand' or general offsider.

If you feel more capable in laying blocks or bricks, then consider utilising these materials in as many walls and partitions as possible.

The 'Organiser Only' Owner Builder

The inexperienced and 'organiser only' Owner Builder is wise to engage the services of a registered Builder, Carpenter, or Building Consultant to carry out weekly inspections on the site. Written instructions should be provided for the Owner Builder to follow.

These should include:

1. Stages to order material and manpower.
2. Any work that needs to be rectified.
3. Any 'along the way' advice.

The 'organiser only' Builder can sometimes continue to hold down his normal job and supervise the building work after hours. He employs subtrades to carry out the work according to plans and specifications.

In this situation, it is of utmost importance that the plans and specifications contain as much detail and instruction as possible for the tradesman to follow during the Owner Builder's absence.

Salient Points to Consider:

1. Beware of employing labour on an hourly basis if one is expected to be absent from the site for long periods.
2. Always ask for quotations and in writing. If quotations have been supplied, ensure the Tradesmen are given to understand clearly all that is required of them beforehand. Give these instructions in writing.

If the house is of a complicated design and a number of contingencies are envisaged, then have the quotations supplied on all those areas where it is possible to quantify and quote. Allow a contingency sum for extras. Seek advice on what amounts to allow for these extras.

Plans

It is advisable that the Owner Builder strongly resist the temptation to obtain house plans cheaply.

I would recommend that the Draftsman or Architect be instructed to provide drawings that an Owner Builder can easily comprehend.

Essential elements that should be included in the working drawings are listed on Page 8 and should be given to the Draftsman or Architect. A lot of misunderstandings can be avoided as well as savings in time and material costs if thoroughly prepared working drawings and large sectional sketches are prepared. Whilst cost saving is necessary there are a few areas in construction where marginally extra spending can provide additional security during freak weather. It must be remember that building bylaws are only the Legal Minimum Requirements designed for average conditions for a particular area. Extra anchor bolts, straps, braces and nails are minimal extra expense but can prove their worth during extreme weather conditions.

Building Abbreviations

AL	Aluminium	MS	Mild Steel	WPM	Waterproof Membrane
AC	Asbestos Cement	NGL	Natural Ground Level	WI	Wrought Iron
BK	Brick	N	North		
BWK	Brickwork	OG	Obscure Glass		
BV	Brick Veneer	O	Oven		

Drainage Abbreviations

CANT	Cantilever	QUAD	Quadrant Moulding	BV	Back Vent
CP	Chrome Plated	REINF	Reinforcing	CIP	Cast Iron Pipe
CORR I	Corrugated Iron	REFRIG	Refrigerator	EV	Educt Vent
CPD	Cupboard	RPD	Real Property	EW	Earthenware
DPC	Damp proof Course		Description	GEW	Glazed Earthenware
DW	Dishwasher	RHS	Rolled Hollow Section	GIT	Grease Inspection Trap
EML	Expanded Metal Lath	RSJ	Rolled Steel Joist	GT	Gully Trap
EJ	Expansion Joint	SAA	Standard Assoc. of	IC	Inspection Chamber
FC	Fibre Cement		Australia	IO	Inspection Opening
FFL	Finished Floor Level	SHR	Shower	JU	Jump Up
FLR	Floor	SD	Sliding Door	PJC	Plain Junction Cap
FW	Floor Waste	SWD	Softwood	P PAN	Allows the outlet to
GAL	Galvanizing	SP	Stand Pipe		project through the rear
G/L	Ground Level	SPEC	Specification		wall
HBD	Hardboard	SC	Stopcock	RWH	Rain Water Head
HT	Height	SV	Stop Valve	S PAN	Allows the outlet to
HWD	Hardwood	TEL	Telephone		drop through the floor
HW	Hot Water	VB	Vapour Barrier		below
INSUL	Insulation	VP	Vent Pipe	SD	Sewer Drain
LVR	Louvre	VENT	Ventilator	SP	Soil Pipe
M	Metre	WBD	Wallboard	SVP	Soil Vent Pipe
MSB	Main Switch Board	WR	Wardrobe	SWD	Storm Water Drain
MANUF	Manufacturer	WM	Washing Machine	WC	Water Closet

Buying Land

(See also HSOB pages 12-15)

Points to consider:

1. Proximity to services such as schools, shops and transport.
2. Could any proposed development such as a freeway or block of flats, etc. adversely affect resale value of your property.
3. It is foolish to put an expensive house on cheap land. Conversely, it is not wise to put a very cheap house on expensive land.
4. Will the rates on the land prove to be prohibitive in relation to your income. If so, look at land in a less exclusive area.
5. "Stop, look and listen" are three words in the landbuyers vocabulary. Noisy neighbours, an illkept neighbourhood or a streetful of dogs could also be part of the package deal.
6. Is the title available on purchase? It is almost impossible to raise a mortgage without this piece of paper. It is not always readily available on new subdivisions.
7. Are there any restrictive convenants on the land? As with No. 6, ensure the Solicitor checks this item also before you sign.
8. Check with the council regarding position of sewer lines etc. These could have to be redirected at your expense.
9. Ensure all boundary pegs are in position and are actually the pegs of your property. This is of utmost importance. Each peg will have the lot

No. carved into it. Boundary pegs that are missing are costly to have replaced by a surveyor.
10. Is the site subject to flooding or tidal surge?
11. Could the site be subject to subsidence due to mining?
12. Has the land been deep filled?
13. Could it be resumed by a Govt. body?
14. Is it subject to a building covenant?
15. Is it beneath a flight path?

Look for:

1. Springs or presence of water courses in the wet season.
2. Slope of land is always greater than the eyes estimate. This increases the cost of the subfloor structure. When this cost is added to initial outlay for land your purchase may be expensive indeed.
3. Before purchasing, obtain some idea of what the subsoil consists of. Enquire at the local Council or ask neighbours if the subsoil is rock or clay. The Council or Developer can provide details on whether the site contains fill. NOTE-fill on house sites can sometimes be many metres deep and this in turn, can incur a great increase on foundation and footing costs. Better still, and for your own peace of mind, have a Soil Engineer carry out a pre-purchase test bore. The purchase contract can be made conditional on the results of the Soil Engineer's report.

Cost Saving Pointers

1. Open living areas reduce costs.
2. Keep plumbing together such as kitchen sink, bath, W.C., laundry: preferably on the one side of the house.
3. Concrete slabs can be cheaper on a level or near level site. However, as the landfall increases, it is more economical to use timber floors. If ground falls dictate a basement height of approximately 1.5m, it would be practical to increase the basement to a useable height of 2.4m. The area then becomes useable garage or living space.

What Type of House Structure to Build

Large skeletal drawings have been especially prepared to assist those people undecided as to what type of construction to adopt. See pages 12-16.

Positioning the House on Site

Decide which rooms you prefer to receive maximum sunlight in winter and cool breezes in summer. An ideal guide is for kitchen and breakfast rooms to be located at the eastern end to receive morning sun, then lounge and if possible, main bedroom facing north. Try to expose remaining living and sleeping rooms to as much northern and eastern aspect as possible. Avoid positioning the kitchen on the western wall.

Positioning the House

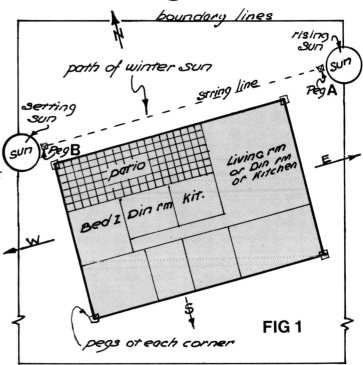

FIG 1

How to Site the House for Aspect

Using figure 1 as an example, establish a string line along the east-west (or sunpath line) across your land. Then peg the 4 corners of the house parallel to that line. If a site receives or requires a more easterly aspect, adjust the 4 corners of the house accordingly.

Having Plans Drawn

It is advisable before approaching a draftsman or architect to have at least established the floor plan 1:50 (or 1/4") scale. Remember to include the thickness of the walls.

Also indicate the following:
1. Position and size of the windows and doors.
2. Direction doors are to swing.
3. Size and position of all prime cost items: that is, bath, shower, vanity, sink, stove, hot water system, fridge, tub, etc.

Important

House plans are a legal document and should be prepared by a Professional. Drafting one's own house plans often places the Owner Builder out of harmony with the local Building Inspector because the inadequate details place an extra workload on him.

Plans with the specifications should contain details of material sizes and methods of construction. This is particularly important to the owner builder. A scanty plan that will pass minimum council requirements will cause nothing but frustration and can result in very costly errors for owner builders. The draftsman or architect should be requested to include the following details in the plans:

1. *Position, type and number of reinforcing steel or mesh in foundation floor, walls and lintels.*
2. *Type and size of all anchor rods or straps should be specified and their positioning clearly defined.*
3. *Type and position of all wall bracing indicated on elevations and floor plan whether steel angle, flat strap, plywood, timber or other.*
4. *Existing ground falls or contours and proposed finished ground falls should be indicated on each elevation by dotted and solid lines.*
5. *All timber sizes and types defined. For example, 100 x 50mm F11 HWD and their spacings.*
6. *Types and spacings of fixings to be used on all roof battens, roof and wall sheathings.*
7. *All abbreviations and symbols interpreted on the plan.*

Types of Fixings

Most plans usually say 'fixed according to Manufacturer's specifications'. This instruction is not adequate for owner builders. The bolt, screw or nail type should be spelled out. The use of incorrect fixings can cause untold problems when local building inspectors require their replacement.

Kitchens Layouts

The hub of the home is still where food is prepared, the kitchen. Considerable thought should be devoted to designing this room. Three governing factors must be considered. The first is the refrigerator because of its size and the direction its door opens; secondly, the sink and stove and/or oven. Sinks are more suitably positioned in front of a window and stoves should not be too distant from the sink.
(See also HSOB pages 16,17)

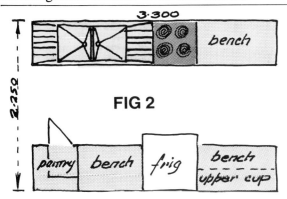

FIG 2

Corridor Kitchens figure 2

Especially ideal where space is limited. Everything is handy but the kitchen tends to become a thoroughfare.

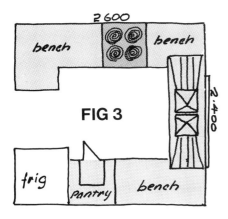

FIG 3

Enclosed Kitchen

Of all designs, this is the most space efficient. Plenty of bench space, adequate storage and minimum exertion required to reach essential points.

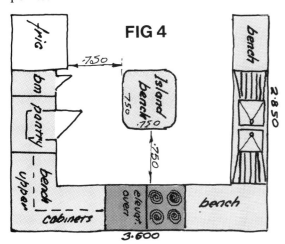

FIG 4

Farmhouse Kitchens figure 4

A large amount of space is required necessitating a lot of walking to reach the various parts of the kitchen.

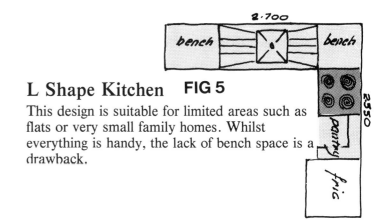

L Shape Kitchen   FIG 5

This design is suitable for limited areas such as flats or very small family homes. Whilst everything is handy, the lack of bench space is a drawback.

Bathroom Layouts

Bathrooms

The average bathroom has a typical dimension of 1.8m x 2.4m. This allows a shower and bath to be positioned along the 2.4m wall. If space permits, a 4-way bathroom is excellent for families permitting all facilities to be used at one time. However, obscure glass panels are required above 2050mm height up to the ceiling to permit illumination to pass to the shower and vanity areas. See figure 8

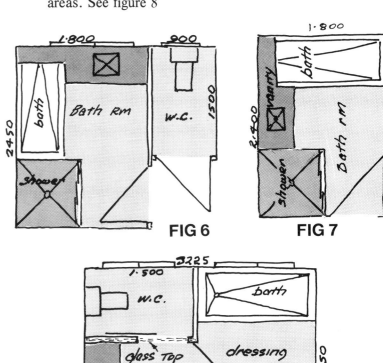

FIG 6   **FIG 7**

FIG 8

Reading Plans

Obtaining Ground Lines

To find ground lines on a sloping site and to transfer on to the elevation drawings:

Step 1 Peg the proposed corners of the house.

Step 2 Drive a peg until its top arrives at the proposed floor level.

Step 3 Using a Builders' tripod level, establish the natural ground levels (N.G.L.) at each corner, whether below or above the floor level peg.

Mark these heights on the house plan elevations.

Join these points together with a dashed line through the elevations and mark N.G.L. on them.

Site Plans

The site plan should be drawn in ink to a minimum of 1:200 scale and should contain the following:

1. Minimum distances from boundaries.
2. Real property description and lot number, etc.
3. Roofing downpipe outlets shown as 'D.P'.
4. North direction.
5. Street position and name.

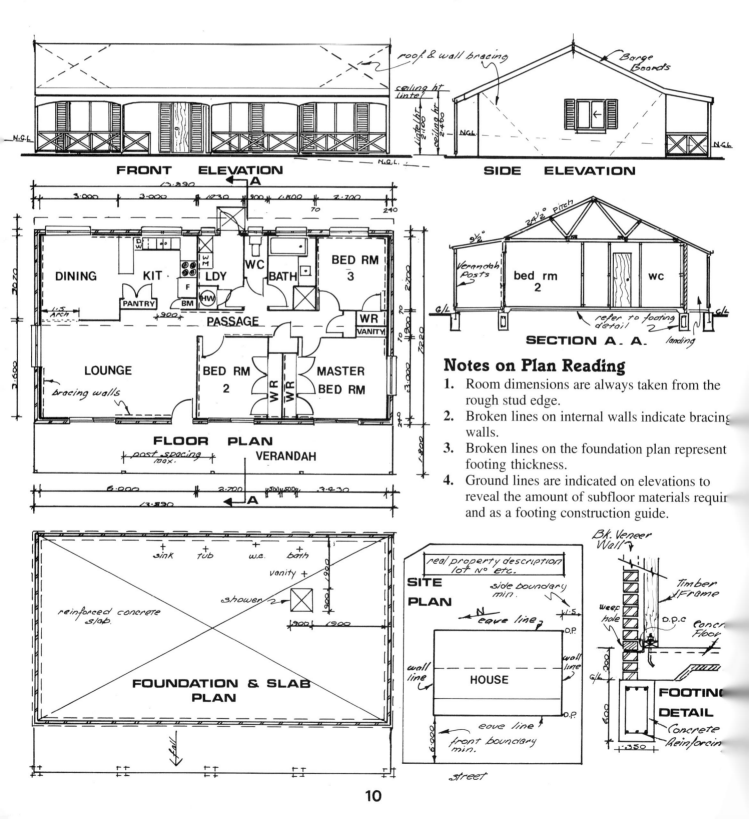

Notes on Plan Reading

1. Room dimensions are always taken from the rough stud edge.
2. Broken lines on internal walls indicate bracing walls.
3. Broken lines on the foundation plan represent footing thickness.
4. Ground lines are indicated on elevations to reveal the amount of subfloor materials requir and as a footing construction guide.

Typical Walls & Footings

The following five pages are intended to familiarise the Owner Builder with the various common types of house construction from which to choose. The footing and wall sections on this and the following page illustrate some of the common designs used.

FIG 9A

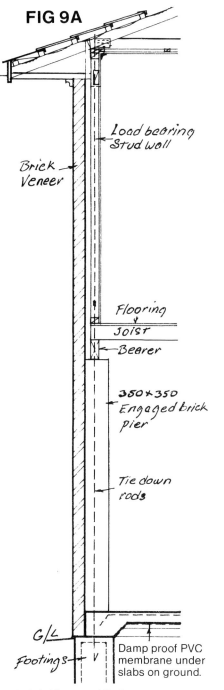

Load bearing Stud wall

Brick Veneer

Flooring
Joist
Bearer

350×350 Engaged brick pier

Tie down rods

G/L
Footings

Damp proof PVC membrane under slabs on ground.

Brick Veneer Highset With Slab Floor
The highset house, although largely replaced by single storey, has superior qualities in that the floor space can be doubled without additional roof & foundation costs, it uses less land area, increases views, breezes & security from burglars. The base is used for laundry, garages, workshops, rumpus & office use (not for living areas) see HSOB for more details.

FIG 9B

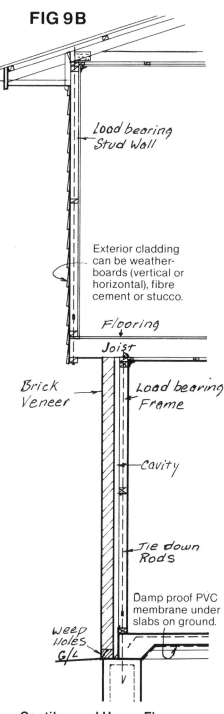

Load bearing Stud Wall

Exterior cladding can be weatherboards (vertical or horizontal), fibre cement or stucco.

Flooring
Joist

Brick Veneer

Load bearing Frame

Cavity

Tie down Rods

Damp proof PVC membrane under slabs on ground.

Weep Holes
G/L

Cantilevered Upper Floor or Brick Veneer Base
This provides living areas downstairs & the cantilevered floor reduces the area of the land required for building. The upper walls are cladded timber frame.

FIG 9C

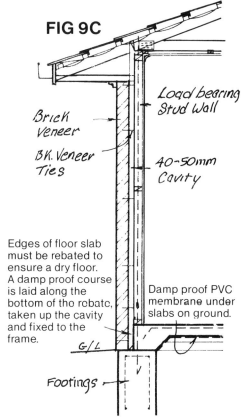

Brick Veneer

BK. Veneer Ties

Load bearing Stud Wall

40-50mm Cavity

Edges of floor slab must be rebated to ensure a dry floor. A damp proof course is laid along the bottom of the robate, taken up the cavity and fixed to the frame.

Damp proof PVC membrane under slabs on ground.

G/L

Footings

Low Set Brick Veneer with Slab Floor
This is the most popular method of wall construction in the eastern & southern states of Australia & provides a maintenance free wall surface.

FIG 10

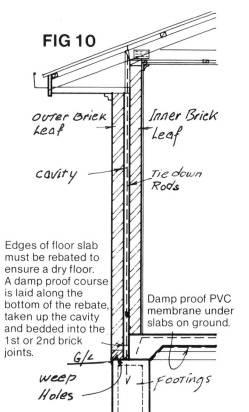

Outer Brick Leaf

Inner Brick Leaf

cavity

Tie down Rods

Edges of floor slab must be rebated to ensure a dry floor. A damp proof course is laid along the bottom of the rebate, taken up the cavity and bedded into the 1st or 2nd brick joints.

Damp proof PVC membrane under slabs on ground.

G/L

weep Holes

V Footings

Cavity (Double Brick) with Slab Floor
Western Australia has adopted this method to a major extent however, in the other states it is the most expensive option.

11

Cont.

FIG 11

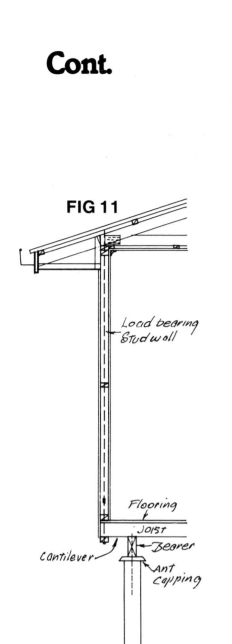

Load bearing Stud wall

Flooring

Joist

Bearer

Cantilever

Ant Capping

Posts set in no fines concrete.
Timber posts should be treated to H5 min.

Top sloped away all round to prevent ponding.

G/L

Timber Frame on Concrete, Steel, or Timber Columns

This method of building is practical where it is desirable to have a 2-storey or highset house at a later date as funds become available. The downstairs areas can be kept exposed for an indefinite period or walls constructed either outside of or between the columns.

FIG 12A

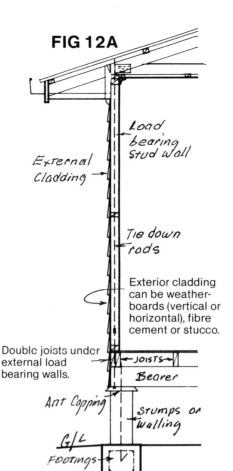

Load bearing Stud Wall

External Cladding

Tie down rods

Exterior cladding can be weather-boards (vertical or horizontal), fibre cement or stucco.

Double joists under external load bearing walls.

JOISTS

Bearer

Ant Capping

Strumps or Walling

G/L

Footings

Clad Timber Frame on Timber Floor on Brick or Block Base

Same as Fig 12B except that the timber floor is mainly practical on sloping sites, is colder in Winter and generally more expensive.

FIG 13

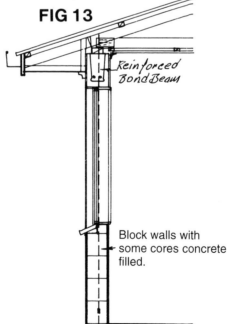

Reinforced Bond Beam

Block walls with some cores concrete filled.

G/L

Damp proof PVC membrane under slabs on ground.

Concrete Block Masonry with a Slab Floor

Applied mostly in North Qld. HSOB should be consulted for detailed building procedures.

FIG 12B

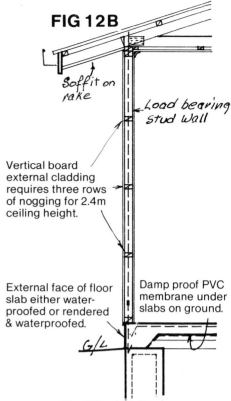

Soffit on rake

Load bearing stud Wall

Vertical board external cladding requires three rows of nogging for 2.4m ceiling height.

External face of floor slab either water-proofed or rendered & waterproofed.

Damp proof PVC membrane under slabs on ground.

G/L

Clad Timber Frame on Slab Floor

This is the most economical method in the short term, however painting every 8-10 years will bring it up to the cost of the brick.

FIG 14

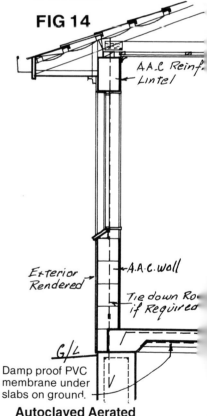

A.A.C. Reinf. Lintel

Exterior Rendered

A.A.C. wall

Tie down Rod if Required

G/L

Damp proof PVC membrane under slabs on ground.

Autoclaved Aerated Concrete Block Walls

This material is marketed under names such as CSR Hebel, & Atlas Thermolite.
The material provides superior insulation, fire protection & weight reduction above all other material & is easy to construct for the Owner Builder, see 'House Building the Easy Hebel Way'.

The Timber Framed House

The timber framed house with external linings fixed directly to the frame will ideally suit the Owner Builder who is inclined towards carpentry.
This system will certainly cut initial building costs. The timber house frame can also be the structural shell for brick veneer.

These two systems of construction are the most popular in Australia and consequently are discussed more comprehensively throughout the manual.
The walls can be constructed on a concrete slab (the simplest means) or over a half or full basement as illustrated using a natural timber or particle board floor (the latter being more commonly used today).

Ant capping should be provided directly beneath the lowest timber floor framing members.

The timber frame can be lined with timber weatherboards or fibre cement sheeting as well as Hardiplank are usually used. Other suggestions would be compressed wood planks such as Weathertex. Stud walls are sometimes cement stuccoed and pleasing effects can be achieved. The application is carried out by a Solid Plasterer. Studs are papered and wired and two coats of cement render are applied. Decorative textures are sprayed over the surface.

Refer to page 45 for further information on timber and HSOB pages 95-98.

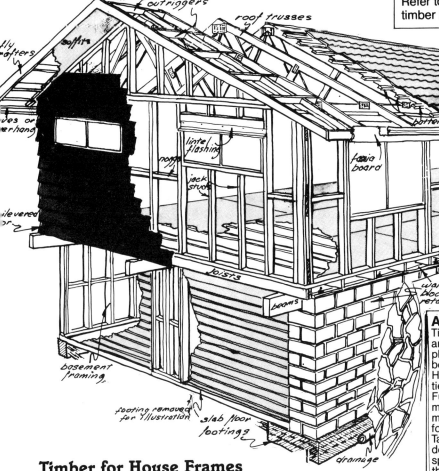

FIG 15

Anchoring Timber Houses
Timber framing members are attached to one another by nails; that is roof members to wall top plates; top and bottom wall plates to studs; bottom plates to floor joists; joists to bearers. However, nailing alone is insufficient to anchor or tie the building together in high wind conditions. Further anchorage means are required and they must be continuous or effective from the roof members to wall framing to floor framing to foundations.
Take careful notice of the methods of anchoring described throughout the manual and the spacings your plans and specifications require them to be positioned at.

Timber for House Frames

Hardwood

Although generally heavier than Pine and harder to nail and saw, its higher 'F' ratings enable smaller sectional sizes to be utilised, thereby reducing costs. Nailing of members e.g. joists etc, often require predrilling to avoid splitting.

Radiata & Slash Pine

Both are easy timbers to nail and saw and good for house framing.

Cyprus Pine

This is an indigenous timber of light weight and easy to work. It has the least shrinkage problem of all Australian timber and is resistant to termite and borer.
When nailing in a dry state, care must be taken to avoid splitting.

Stages of Construction

1. Foundation and basement walls.
2. Concrete floors or bearers, joists and floor laid.
3. Wall frames erected.
4. Roof framing constructed plus fascia and barge boards fitted.
5. Roof sarked and cladded.
6. Windows and exterior doors installed.
7. External cladding applied and soffits lined.
8. Ceilings battened or/and nogged.
9. Plumbing pipes and electrical wiring installed.
10. Ceilings and walls lined.
11. Bath shower and kitchen cupboards installed.
12. Doors and all mouldings fitted.
13. Plumbing finished off.
14. Painting and decorating.
15. Floors sanded.
16. Electrical work finished off.

13

Brick Veneer Construction

FIG 16

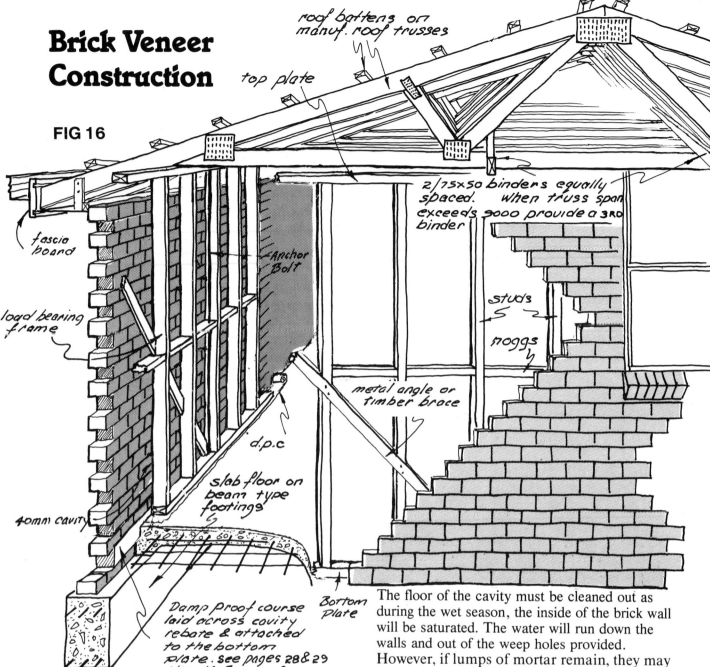

roof battens on manuf. roof trusses

top plate

fascia board

load bearing frame

Anchor Bolt

2/75x50 binders equally spaced. when truss span exceeds 9000 provide a 3rd binder

studs

noggs

metal angle or timber brace

d.p.c

slab floor on beam type footings

40mm cavity

Damp proof course laid across cavity rebate & attached to the bottom plate. see pages 28&29 also HSOB 38-41 & 104

Bottom Plate

What is Brick Veneer?

It is a brick facade anchored to a timber frame with metal or wire ties regularly spaced . The timber frame does all the structural load bearing work supporting the roof, ceiling and wall linings. A 40mm air space or cavity is provided between the frame and brick wall. This cavity acts also as a water barrier.

When is the Brick Wall Constructed?

This is done in two stages. The first after the footings are complete. Brickwork is laid and terminated just below floor level. The second after the roof is framed and the eaves constructed, windows framed and meter box installed. Interior linings should not be fixed until the veneer is complete. This is essential as access to the cavity is necessary in order to clean out mortar droppings. After eaves framing is constructed, windows and door frames can be installed. Then brickwork can be continued. Prior to lining the inside surface of the frame, ensure all mortar droppings have been cleaned from veneer ties.

The floor of the cavity must be cleaned out as during the wet season, the inside of the brick wall will be saturated. The water will run down the walls and out of the weep holes provided. However, if lumps of mortar remain, they may form a bridge for water to cross and so cause dry rot to the structural frame.

Where sheet bracing is applied on the cavity side, the cavity is kept clean by laying battens to catch the mortar droppings.

Stages of Construction

1. Foundations and footings
2. Brick Base to Floor Level
3. Floor Laid Either Concrete or Timber
4. Timber Wall Frames Erected
5. Roof Framing Completed, Tiles & Sheathing Attached
6. Windows & External Doors Installed
7. Brick Veneer Walls Completed.
8. Soffits framed and sheeted
9. Electrical Wiring & Plumbing Pipe Out with Drainage Carried Out Also
10. Ceilings and Walls Lined
11. Internal Doors, Bath, Shower, Kitchen Cupboards and all Mouldings Fitted
12. Plumbing & P.C. Items Completed
13. Decorating
14. Electrical Fittings & Switches Installed
15. Floor Sanding & Carpets Laid

14

Concrete Block Construction

Concrete block construction can be a very economical and quick alternative for the Owner Builder, particularly if the block surface is simply waterproofed and painted.

Linings can be easily fixed to the blockwork internally. Partitions are constructed in timber or 100 or 150mm blocks.

Timber bracing partitions are bolted to block walls at 600mm centres and the end stud strapped to its top and bottom plates. Other partitions may be hand or ramset nailed. Cooperation will be required by the Plumber, Electrician and Carpenter whilst block work is in progress for the installation of services through and down the block cores.

Stages in Construction

1. Footings
2. Any blockwork below slab level.
3. Slab is poured with all relevant drainage and plumbing services installed prior to pouring.
4. Blockwork with steel reinforcing, external doors and windows, plumbing and electrical conduits installed.
5. Concrete grout is poured to applicable vertical cores, lintels and bond beams.
6. Construct fireplace and chimney, if any, Erect internal partitions, then roof framing and eaves.
7. Attach sarking and cladding to roof.
8. Install bath and shower.
9. Line or solid plaster internal walls and ceilings.
10. Install internal doors, kitchen cupboards, mouldings, tiling etc.
11. Seal and paint exterior blockwork or stucco surfaces.

Block wall construction can also be combined with a timber floor.

For further information on 'Block Construction', see Pages 94,95. (See also HSOB Pages 58-65).

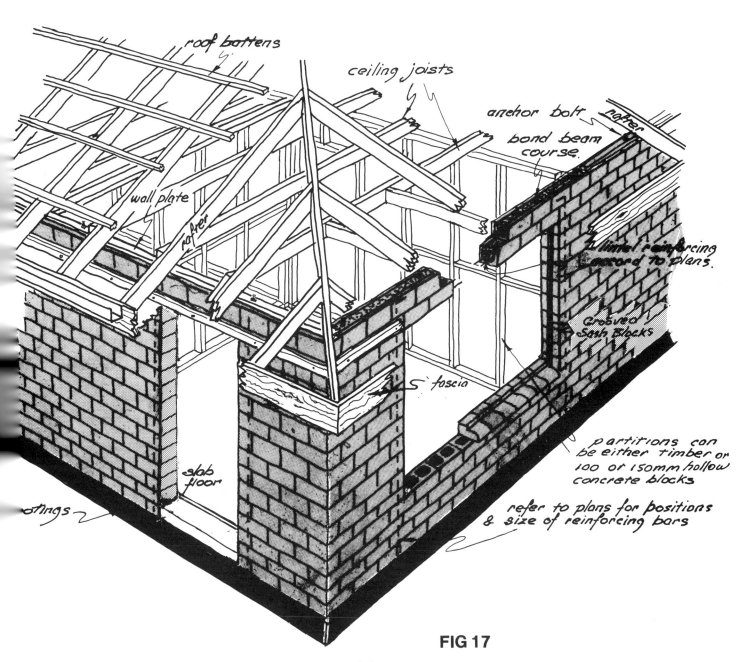

FIG 17

15

Cavity Brick Construction

What is Cavity Brick

Cavity brick construction is simply 2 brick walls standing side by side separated by a 40mm - 50mm cavity and tied together with brick ties that cross the cavity embedded into the mortar joints.

The inner leaf can be finished as face bricks or common bricks can be used and walls solid plastered or lined with wallboard. Floor can either be concrete slab or timber.

Internal partitions can also be brick and finished in a similiar manner or 75mm timber frame partitions can be used and wallboard lining attached. In the case where timber partitions butt against exterior brick walls, the end stud is secured to the inner brick skin by ramset nails or in the case of bracing partitions, the end stud is bolted to the inner brick skin at 600mm centres and is also strapped to its top and bottom plate.

An alternative is to use brick as the outer skin and 100mm concrete block on the inner skin. Costs are reduced especially if the blocks remain as a painted surface. Cavity ties are applied the same as for double brick walls.

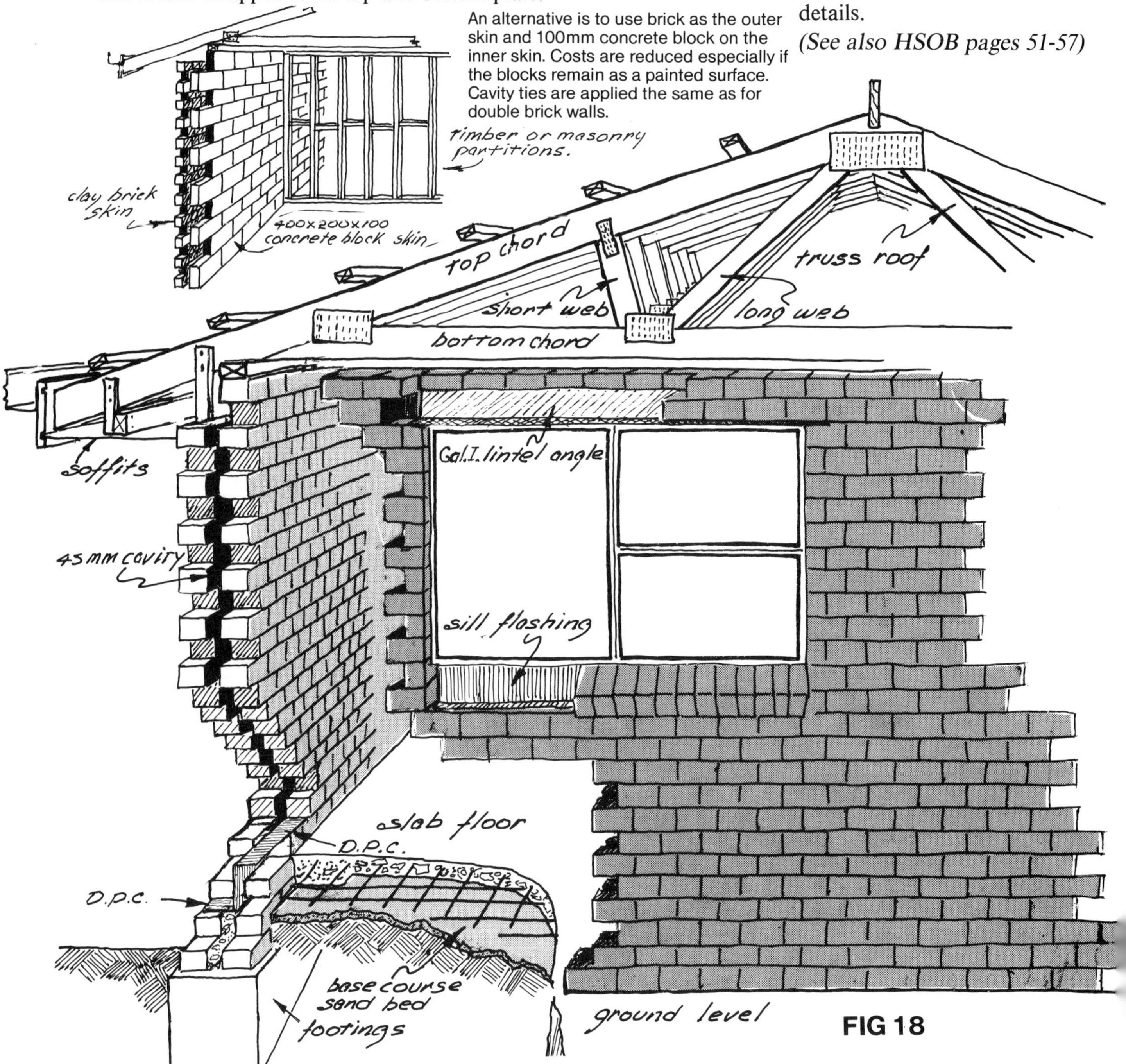

Stages of Construction

1. Footings are laid with reinforcing rods inserted.
2. Bricks are laid up to slab floor level or when using a timber floor, up to bottom of bearer height.
3. Floor is laid.
4. The inner leaf of the double wall is built
5. Internal partitions constructed.
6. Roof erected and sheathed.
7. Internal linings attached and all doors fitted and finishing work carried out.
   At the same time the outer brick leaf on the double brick walls are built

See pages 96 & 97 for further details.

(See also HSOB pages 51-57)

timber or masonry partitions.

clay brick skin

400x200x100 concrete block skin

top chord

short web

long web

truss roof

bottom chord

soffits

Gal.I. lintel angle

45mm cavity

sill flashing

slab floor
D.P.C.

D.P.C.

base course
sand bed
footings

ground level

FIG 18

Do's & Don'ts when Employing Subcontractors or Employees *(See also 'HSOB' Pages 8,9, 91-93)*

Do's & Don'ts

1. Do be courteous and respect the Tradesman. Remember he is a trained specialist in his field whose skill you need.

2. Don't be aggressive in your requests to workmen on the site. This engenders hard feelings and undoubtedly will lose co-operation and harmony.

3. Do leave tradesman alone to carry out their work, if and when your assistance is not required. If you must inspect their work while it is in progress, do so unobtrusively.

4. Beware of supplying Subcontractors with second-hand or used materials. It makes all Tradesmen discontented even if you are paying them extra to use them.

5. If paying wages, do so at the same time every week. It is best to have wages drawn the day before or at least 8 hours in advance.

6. If you are employing workmen on a hourly rate, do not cut their tea or lunch breaks short. This creates discontentment.

It is good practice to decide which Subcontractors you are using before commencing any work on site.

When accepting quotations, discuss approximate dates for them to commence work. Liaise with Subcontractors throughout every stage.

Obtaining Quotations & Making Payments

Obtaining Quotations

1. It is usual to obtain two or three quotations.

2. Make all the conditions clear, any alterations to the plan, method of payment whether weekly or in stages.

3. Ask if the Subcontractors will provide addresses of any work previously completed for inspection by yourself or a Tradesman.

4. Beware of subcontractors who are only temporarily in the district.

5. Have all quotations in writing and signed.

6. After accepting the quotation, make an agreement in writing on the quotation stating method of payment, whether in weekly draws or at specific stages, including the date and the signatures of both parties.

Further Instructions

Clarify with the Subcontractor the following:

1. Does he possess a current Contractors' Licence and will the licence allow him to carry out the contract (some licences have limitations).

2. Does he possess current and adequate insurance cover for his employees and third party cover.

3. Which party is to provide and erect any scaffolding.

4. Which party is to perform the cleaning up of the site during construction and on completion.

Keeping Records

It is vitally important to keep all records such as:

Receipts, Inspection Certificates or slips, order numbers, guarantees, cheque butts, concrete dockets (stating the quality, strength and slump figures), and Termite Treatment certificates, etc.

Use a portable expandable file which can be kept in your vehicle at the site during construction.

Making Payment

It is common practice to make payment to Subcontractors either weekly or in stages for work thus far completed. Arrange for an account stating material and labour used to that stage.

Do everything in writing.

Where tradeswork can only be completed in part, it is acceptable practice to retain 5-10% of monies until the remaining work is completed.

5-10% of monies can sometimes be held for 30 days from some manufactured goods where faults could arise within 30 days.

Where inspection of work is to be carried out by any Authorities, withhold payment until such inspections are made.

Local Council Inspections are generally carried out for the following stages:

1.	Footings	2.	Slab Floor
3.	Frame	4.	Completion of House

Estimating Totals

Approaching Lending Authorities

The Owner Builder who presents details to the Lending Authority in a well presented manner will receive more favourable consideration for finance. The proposed plan should be submitted accompanied by a typed list such as the one set out below and supported by Sub-contractor's written quotations.

Lending Authorities will give higher priority to the Owner Builder who can submit estimated dates of: A. Commencement B. Roof Completion C. Finishing

The following items will cover most types of construction. Rule a line through items that are not applicable. Most Hardware Merchants and Tradesmen will give a 'take-off quote' on the plan but it still remains your responsibility to check that all items are included in the quotation.

Labour & Materials   QUOTE $

Excavations
Allow per hour + Travelling
Bulldozer & Backhoe
Chaindigger for footings
Bobcat to level slab
Truck Hire to remove fill
Fill if required
Labour

Footings & Slab
Steel Trench Mesh
Stirrups & Starter Bars
Lengths of Steel Bars
Slab Mesh, Tie Wires &
    Bar Chairs
Concrete Stumps
Ground Poisoning
Labour

Concrete For:
Footings
Slab or Suspended Floor
Cement Grout
Drives and Paths
Column Bases
Labour

Steelwork
U Beams
Steel and Open Web Joists
M S Angles & Flats
Steel Step Stringers
Plates & Saddles
Welder's Labour

Timber
Profiles, Formwork (Boxing)
    & Pegs
Subfloor Framing:
Bottom & Top Plates
    & Noggs
Studs
Lintels
Bracing
Floor Framing:
Wall Plates
Bearers & Beams
Laminated Beams
Floor Joists & Bridging
Herringbone Strutting

Nogging for Flooring
Verandah Plates, Joists
Verandah Flooring

Wall Framing
Top & Bottom Plates
    & Noggs
Studs
Window Sills
Door Heads
Wall Plates for Brick Walls
Bracing

Roof Framing
Roof Trusses & Anchoring
    Hardware
Ceiling Joists & Noggs
Ceiling Binders
Hanging Beams
Strutting Beams
Exposed Beams
Laminated Beams
Rafters & Hip, Ridge
    & Valley Rafters
Valley Boards
Collar Ties
Under Purlins
Struts
King Posts
Bracing
Dragon Ties
Fascia Boards
Barge Boards
Gable Framing
Sundry Timber

External Wall Claddings
Chamferboards or
    Weatherboards
Vertical Cedar
Weathertex
Hardiplank
Any Other Claddings

Carpenter's Labour to:
Set Out Profiles
Cut Out & Erect Subfloor
    Framing
Bearers, Joists, Flooring
Cut & Erect Wall and Roof
    Framing

Labour & Materials   QUOTE $

Fix Gable Ends & Soffits
Exterior Wall Linings
Interior Wall Linings
Install Battenings or
    Claddings to Basement
Erecting Scaffolds
Install Bath, Shower,
    Cabinets & Pantry
    Wardrobes, Linen
    Cupboards

Brickwork

Brick Base and Veneer
Steps
Arches
Veneer Ties, Cavity Ties
Cement Sand & Lime
Labour

Blockwork

Concrete Blocks
Steel Reinforcing Rods
Cement, Sand & Lime
Plasticiser
Labour

Roofing

Battens, Tiles
Cladding & Moulds
Sarking
Skylights & Ventilators
Labour

Plumber

Labour & Material

Drainer

Sewerage or Septic
Stormwater & Surface
    Drainage
Labour

Electrician

Light and other fittings
Labour and Materials

Internal Linings

Plasterboard
Plasterer's Labour
Material
F.C. Sheeting or Tempered
    Hardboard for:
Soffit Linings
Garage Linings
Sheeting behind tiling
Ceilings
Walls
Gables
Insulation
Tiles & Materials
Tilers Labour
Laminex Linings to:
Kitchen Cupboards
Shower

Labour & Materials   QUOTE $

Around Bath
Bench Tops and Laundry

Floor Sander

Painting   Material & Labour

Hardware

Nails, Screws & Hinges
Anchor Bolts
Metal Angle Bracing
Door Handles & Locks
    & Stops
Glue & Sealants
Primers, Sandpaper
Waterproofing Agents
Soffit Ventilators

Prime Cost Items

Stove
Hot Water System
Solar Hot Water System
Kitchen Sink
Laundry Tub, Cabinet
    W.C. Vanity Unit
    or Handbasins
Clothes Hoist
Bath
Shower Tray

Doors

Exterior solid or hollow
Interior hollow or special
Garage plus jambs and
    fittings

Windows

Hiring Gear

Jackhammer/kanga
Power Pole, Extension
    Cables
Power Saws and Sawbench
Power Drill
Concreting Equipment
Pneumatic Nailing
    Equipment
Scaffolding
Levelling Equipment
Ramset Nailing Gun
Other

Fees & Costs

Plans
Insurance: Contractor'
    All Risk Public Liability
Workers' Compensation
Council Fees & Bonds
Power Pole Fee
Underground Power Fee
Sanitary Cost for
    Temporary W.C.
Rates While Under
    Construction
Loan Fees

Estimating Guide

Some Manufacturers and Suppliers of the following items often provide a measuring and costing service: Timber and Roofing: Windows and Wallboard: Roofing Material: Bricks: External claddings: Kitchen Cupboards: Plumbing: Hardware.

Subcontractors often will supply remaining quantities or quotations. However, knowing how to quantify the following items may prove invaluable.

Estimating Timber Framing

Studs

Indicate with a mark on the floor plan the position of each stud at their correct centres using a scale. Allow 3 studs to every corner plus trimmer studs at sides of windows. Designate trimmer and jack studs above and below windows to be full length common studs. This extra allowance becomes a safety margin. Studs are bought in approximate stud lengths or can be cut to your own requirements.

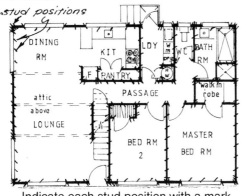

Indicate each stud position with a mark on the floor plan.

Plates and Noggs

Using a scale on the floor plan, add the length of the walls into a total sum. Then multiply this figure by 3. This represents top and bottom plates and 1 row of noggs. Add a further 10% for wastage.

For example – 70m x 3 = 210 + 10% (safety margin for wastage 21m) = 231m total.

If plates or noggs are of different thicknesses, calculate their lengths separately.

Joists, Bearers and Battens

Again using a scale, mark the position of each member on the floor plan at the maximum spacings. Include any joists for wall support and any double joists for end walls. Total the quantity. Joists and bearers are bought in their correct length plus wastage. Battens are bought by the lineal metre.

Rafters and Roof Timbers

Rafter lengths will be found in a rafter tables book or they can be scaled from a plan drawn to large scale. The remaining roof timber can also be scaled from the plans. (Always include a little extra for wastage).

Bricks

There are 56 standard bricks 230mm x 110mm x 76mm to each square metre. This figure includes wastage. Bricks are quantified by multiplying the length of each wall by its height. Multiply the total by 56. See figure 20. For cavity brick, double the figure.

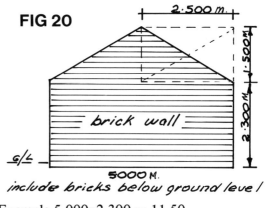

FIG 20

include bricks below ground level

Example 5.000x2.300 = 11.50
2.500x1.500 = 3.75
15.25x56 = 854 bricks

Concrete

To find the cubic metres required, multiply the width by the thickness by the length.

A floor 7.8m x 100mm x 15m = 11.7 cu m allow an extra 5% for waste

A footing 500mm x 350mm x 50m = 8.75 cu m allow an extra 7.5% for waste

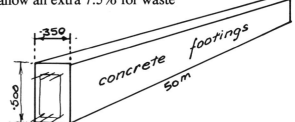

Ready to Go

Tools Required

It is unnecessary for the owner builder to be as tool equipped as the professional builder. Many tools are readily available from hire equipment establishments. Your tool needs will depend on whether you are building in masonry or timber. Buy only tools that will be required frequently. As far as electrical tools go, a 175mm portable electric saw and a 10mm 2 speed drill are a must. The 175mm saw is light enough to use with one hand, yet big enough to cut all timbers in a house frame. Also purchase sufficient extension cable to reach all job extremeties. If there is a lot of masonry work to perform, then it will be necessary to purchase an electrical concrete mixer and a wheelbarrow. Keep the mixer clean as it can be resold later. If it is intended to lay a lot of bricks or blocks, then acquire the appropriate tools. If it is intended to carry out carpentry, work in conjunction with a tradesman. Some basic carpentry tools will be required as tradesmen do not appreciate their tools being continuously borrowed.

Tee up your Subbies:

Prior to commencing construction, the following subcontractors should be organized regarding approximate commencement dates and material needs:
1. Organize excavator and trencher or post hole digger.
2. Electrician (for temporary power)
3. Plumber
4. Drainer
5. Concretor
6. Carpenter
7. Bricklayer

Other subbies to be organized as job progresses:
1. Gyprock fixer and plasterer
2. Roofer
3. Tiler
4. Floor sander
5. Painter

Suppliers to Arrange: Materials: and Approximate Delivery Dates for:
1. Sand, gravel and filling supplier
2. Bricks and blocks
3. Hardware merchant
4. Concrete
5. Timber
6. Roofing
7. Windows and doors and other joinery
8. Tilta and rolla doors
9. Wallboard or plasterboard
10. Kitchen manufacturer
11. Paint and wallpaper
12. Light fittings

Insurances

Three insurances are essential and considered as normal building contracting expenses.

1. Contractors All Risks

This is a policy covering all eventualities on the building site such as damage or loss while under construction, through storm, wind, fire, theft, collapse, explosion, malicious damage and glass breakage. Minimum cover should be for the completed value of the house including labour and should be taken out prior to building commencement

2. Public Liability

Usually this policy can be included as a single package with the Contractors All Risk. It provides financial protection for actions brought against you as a result of your legal responsibility for accidents causing injury, loss, or damage to persons or the property of others. The minimum cover should be discussed with your insurance Company.

Workers Compensation

This insurance is compulsory if one is employing workers on wages even if they are on the site temporarily. If one is engaging subcontractors, ensure they have the current workers compensation policies. Do not neglect to cover yourself.

Ready to Go Check List
1. Ensure title on property is cleared.
2. Ensure finance is approved in writing.
3. Secure your "owner builders licence" from the Authority concerned. See page 4
4. Have plans and specifications approved by the local council.
5. Take out insurances.
6. Erect job sign with lot No., name and owner builder's registration number displayed if this is required.
7. Erect temporary power pole in conjunction with the electrician.
8. Erect temporary W.C. or E.C.
9. Have water connected to the site.

2

Concrete Footings and Slab Floors

Siting the House

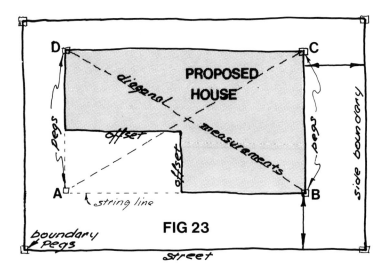

FIG 23

Profiles

Profiles provide a means of accurately aligning, squaring and levelling a house on the site. Prior to digging foundations, the positions of walls and columns have to be accurately defined. This is carried out by first "siting the house" on the land by driving in pegs at the proposed approximate corners of the house See figure 2 3. Profiles consisting of temporary wooden frames erected approximately 1200mm outside footing or pier lines are then constructed. The outside face of all walls are indicated by nails partially driven on the top edges of profiles. String lines are attached to opposite ends of the proposed walls. The top edges of profiles are kept level throughout.

Steps to Siting a House See figure 24

Step 1 Fix a string line to the front and side boundary pegs.

Step 2 Measure back the required distance from the front boundary given on the site plan to the outside face of the house. Fix pegs calling them "A" and "B". See figure 23. These pegs represent the width of the house and must be the correct distance from the side boundary.

Step 3 Find peg "C" by measuring from peg "B". Check to ensure it is the required minimum distance from the back boundary. Peg "D" is found by measuring from "A" and "C". Forget about the offset at this stage if the plan shows one. Roughly square these 4 pegs now by taking measurements diagonally and adjust both rear pegs sideways until both diagonals are the same length.

On Irregular Sites

If the house is parallel to one boundary only: Square the building from this boundary ensuring again the minimum distances (as required by the Council) are maintained from all boundaries.
When the house is not parallel to any boundary:
Step A Establish one side, or front, or rear of the house in the position desired. Ensure minimum distances between house wall and boundary are maintained.

Step B Then proceed to measure off and peg out another wall, using the first wall to square from. Apply the "3, 4, 5," rule.

Step C Establish remaining walls, squaring off the first two. Again check that boundary minimum distances have been adhered to.

The 3,4,5, method of squaring

A right angle can also be established by the 3,4,5, method or their multiples such as 12,16,20 etc. Peg out the right angle roughly using the 2 smallest figures – 3m and 4m. Adjust them until the diagonal measures 5m. For accurate squaring of a large area, use greater multiples.

A 75mm x 25mm timber triangle is commonly used based on the 3,4,5, principal, 1.8m x 2.4m x 3m.

Setting Out Profiles

Erecting Profiles

Firstly drive in the 4 corner profile pegs keeping the tops above the finished level. Then with a builder's tripod level, place a level mark on each peg. Fix a nail on these marks. Then string a line tight around the perimeter attached to these nails. This acts as a guide for fixing the remaining profiles. If the building has an offset such as an L shape, use short sections of profiles at opposite sides of this offset both ways as in figure 24.

Squaring

Mark the front outside wall face position on the profiles. From this line, mark off the rear wall position and repeat the procedure for side walls. Now stretch a string line on nails to these points. Do not worry about offsets (if there are any) until these 4 positions are square. Now to square the area within the string line, take diagonal measurements from the string line intersections as indicated by the dotted line in figure 24. Adjust the 2 rear nails supporting the side wall string lines. Adjust both the same amount until the diagonal measurements correspond. Keep in mind to maintain the legal distance from boundaries. Offsets can be measured from these 4 fixed points.

Transferring Footing Lines to Ground Level

Footings are wider than the walls they support and are centralized beneath those walls. If the site is not level, footing positions must now be transferred to ground level. This is carried out by plumbing a line to pegs sited directly below the footing marks on the profiles. Nails are driven on these marks. String lines are then attached and lime or plaster dust sprinkled beneath the lines to act as a guide for trenching equipment. Only the outside lines of the footing are required as trenching blades are usually the correct trench width. 60mm nails should be used for fixing pegs and braces to the levelling boards. 50mm nails are used to hold the string lines.

Materials

Pegs 50mmx50mm RHWD (Rough sawn hardwood)
Levelling boards 100mmx25mm RHWD
Braces to be 75mmx25mm 75mmx50mm according to height.
Nails

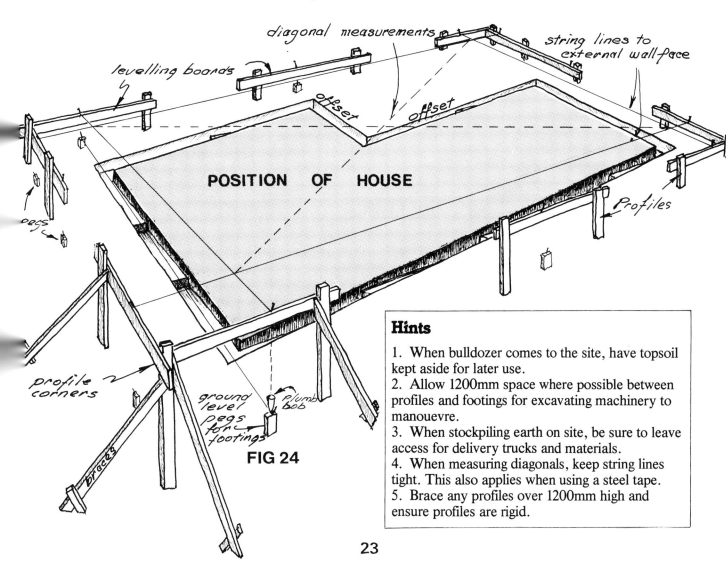

FIG 24

Hints

1. When bulldozer comes to the site, have topsoil kept aside for later use.
2. Allow 1200mm space where possible between profiles and footings for excavating machinery to manouevre.
3. When stockpiling earth on site, be sure to leave access for delivery trucks and materials.
4. When measuring diagonals, keep string lines tight. This also applies when using a steel tape.
5. Brace any profiles over 1200mm high and ensure profiles are rigid.

Footing Preparation

With all footing lines indicated, the footings are now ready for excavating.

Footings are usually excavated using a backhoe or chaindigger. It is uneconomical to excavate firm subsoils by hand and for the Owner Builder this often spells discouragement at the beginning of the project. If on excavation, unexpected soft subsoils are encountered, dig a test hole to determine the depth required to reach a firm bottom. A pier and beam type foundation as in figure 28 may be required. Seek advice from the local Building Inspector.

Excavations

Following the departure of the excavators, clean out footings and square all the corners. Ensure bottom of footings are level.
For any areas excavated too deep, just square corners and level bottoms. Do not be tempted to fill with soil. The extra concrete used is negligible.

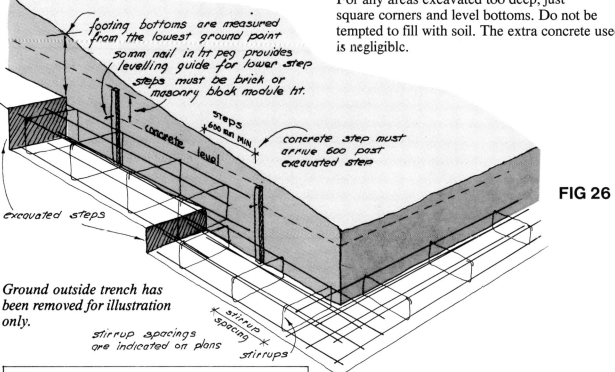

footing bottoms are measured from the lowest ground point

50mm nail in ht peg provides levelling guide for lower step

steps must be brick or masonry block module ht.

steps 600 mm MIN

concrete level

concrete step must arrive 600 past excavated step

excavated steps

FIG 26

Ground outside trench has been removed for illustration only.

stirrup spacing

stirrup spacings are indicated on plans

stirrups

Hint

Avoid the temptation to minimize on material and specifications at foundation stage. Your home is only as secure as the foundations it is placed on. Structural movements will be minimized if these instructions are adhered to.

Height Pegs

Drive 25mm x 25mm RHWD concrete height pegs along the sides of the trench walls every 2.4 - 3m. Nails driven in the sides of the pegs will act as a guide for levelling the wet concrete. Find these level points using a builders tripod level. Where steps in footings occur, keep pegs 600mm in front of the excavated steps and drive a nail to indicate the steps.

FIG 27

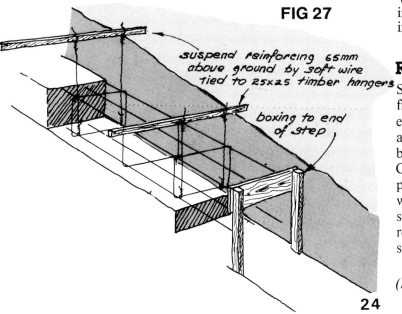

suspend reinforcing 65mm above ground by soft wire tied to 25x25 timber hangers

boxing to end of step

Reinforcing

Suspend reinforcing cages or trenchmesh as in figure 27 Maintain 40mm away from sides and ends of footings and ensure end joins and corners are lapped according to specifications. Install boxing 600mm in front of all steps
Concrete can now be poured. Ensure while pouring that reinforcing is not forced into contact with the trench. Level off concrete using a straightedge. If reinforcing starter bars are required, position these now to a string line stretched between profiles.

(See also HSOB pages 22-26)

Problem Footings

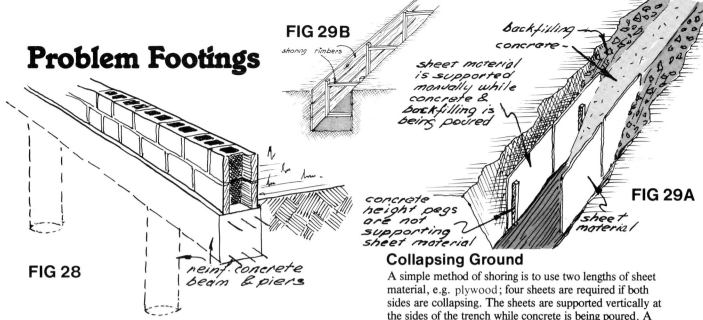

FIG 29B
shoring timbers

backfilling concrete

sheet material is supported manually while concrete & backfilling is being poured

FIG 29A

concrete height pegs are not supporting sheet material

sheet material

FIG 28

reinf. concrete beam & piers

Pier and Beam Foundation

This type of footing is applied where firm subsoils can only be found at a greater depth. For detailed instructions on pier and beam footings see HSOB page 25.

Collapsing Ground

A simple method of shoring is to use two lengths of sheet material, e.g. plywood; four sheets are required if both sides are collapsing. The sheets are supported vertically at the sides of the trench while concrete is being poured. A man back-fills the outside of the trench to the same heights as the rising concrete. As footings are filled, the first two sheets are continually repositioned (see fig.29A) Method Fig. 29B is sometimes necessary. Use demolition timbers to save costs. Keep the bottom strut at ground level; thread reinforcing between struts and remove top strut as the concrete is being poured.

Insitu Concrete Columns
(Stumps)

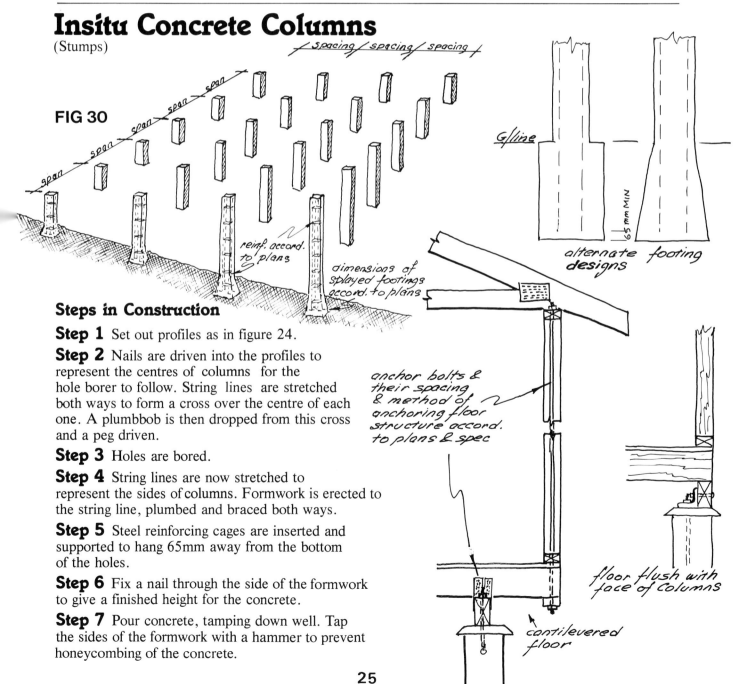

spacing / spacing / spacing

FIG 30

span span span span span span

reinf. accord. to plans

dimensions of splayed footings accord. to plans

G/line

65mm MIN

alternate footing designs

anchor bolts & their spacing & method of anchoring floor structure accord. to plans & spec

cantilevered floor

floor flush with face of columns

Steps in Construction

Step 1 Set out profiles as in figure 24.

Step 2 Nails are driven into the profiles to represent the centres of columns for the hole borer to follow. String lines are stretched both ways to form a cross over the centre of each one. A plumbbob is then dropped from this cross and a peg driven.

Step 3 Holes are bored.

Step 4 String lines are now stretched to represent the sides of columns. Formwork is erected to the string line, plumbed and braced both ways.

Step 5 Steel reinforcing cages are inserted and supported to hang 65mm away from the bottom of the holes.

Step 6 Fix a nail through the side of the formwork to give a finished height for the concrete.

Step 7 Pour concrete, tamping down well. Tap the sides of the formwork with a hammer to prevent honeycombing of the concrete.

Precast Concrete Columns (Stumps)

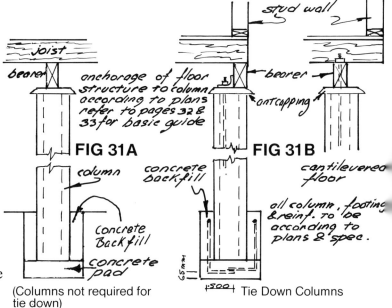

FIG 31A   FIG 31B

anchorage of floor structure to column according to plans refer to pages 32 & 33 for basic guide

(Columns not required for tie down)

Tie Down Columns

all column, footing & reinf. to be according to plans & spec.

Plans and specifications will determine dimensions of columns and those designated for tie down.
Tie down columns are required at specific spacings to anchor the building

Steps in Construction

Step 1 Set out profiles as in figure 24. Nails are driven to indicate centre of columns. String lines are stretched both ways forming a cross over the centre of the column. A plumb bob is dropped from this cross and a peg driven.

Step 2 Holes are dug or drilled to the dimension on plans.

Step 3 Concrete is poured in the bottom of holes to the depth indicated on plans.

Step 4 Precast concrete columns are lowered into holes and aligned to a string line stretched between profiles indicating their sides. Columns are backfilled with concrete as in fig 31A and those required for tie down have reinforcing included as in fig 31B.

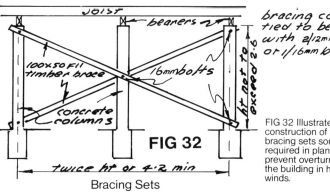

FIG 32

Bracing Sets

bracing columns tied to bearers with 2/12mm bolts or 1/16mm bolt.

FIG 32 Illustrates the construction of timber bracing sets sometimes required in plans to prevent overturning of the building in high winds.

Concrete Block Bases

Steps in Construction

Step 1 Reinforce and pour footings as in pages 24 and 25 but insert starter bars into wet concrete at centres as indicated on plans, following a string line that represents the block centres. Take care in ensuring the bars will arrive in the centre of the block cores.

Step 2 Construct blockwork.

Step 3 Install reinforcing.

Step 4 Pour concrete grout and set anchor bolts for wall plates at each corner beside openings and at 1200mm centres

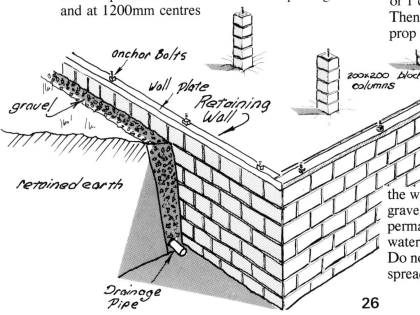

FIG 33

Step 5 Timber wall plates are now fixed in place and floor framing constructed as in chapter 3.

Retaining Walls

> All retaining walls should be designed by an Engineer. However, designs and specifications can be obtained from many concrete block Manufacturers.

Concrete block bases or basements are ideal where the ground is required to be retained. Designated hollow cores are reinforced and concrete filled to support outside earth loads. drainage is provided externally below the first masonry course: the wall is waterproofed with a minimum of 2, preferably 3 coats of Hydroseal or similar bitumen based waterproofing or 1 coat of Tremproof 60 by Pabco.
Then drape polythene sheet over the surface and prop sheets of material such as Hardiflex against the wall to protect the polythene while 10mm gravel is backfilled. The Hardiflex remains permanently; the polythene is a secondary waterproofing measure.
Do not top dress the gravel but allow the grass to spread across naturally, see also HSOB Page 28.

Concrete Slab Floors

Brick veneer combined with a slab floor is most practical when applied to a level or near level site. The surface of the slab should be finished 300mm above finished ground level. State requirements may vary. Check Local Council bylaws. When used in a situation where over 300mm of fill is required, the Council may require Engineer's drawings showing the means of supporting the slab. Costs are immediately increased to provide supporting piers and in most cases, extra steel is needed in the slab or a thickened slab, or both. Alternatively, metal or gravel hard fill can be compacted in 150mm layers with a vibrating compactor. Check for local Council approval. *(See also HSOB pages 27, 52, 53, 61, 101, 102)*

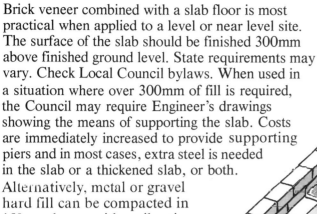

or other methods of forming the slab edge step see page 28, also SOB page 102, fig.97.

FIG 34

Remember a bulldozer can also be used to reduce the ground fall and create a level site for the slab floor. This must be carried out prior to excavating footings. The ground should be graded to fall away from the slab at least 1:20 for a distance of 1.0m around the perimeter of the slab.

How to Construct Slab Floors

Step 1 Prepare footings as previously described.

Step 2 Bricklayers must now be employed to bring brickwork (or blockwork) up to floor level. This acts as formwork for the filling, basecourse and the wet concrete when it is poured.

Step 3 Install any drainage pipes, electrical wiring or heating ducts etc. Erect rebate formwork.

Step 4 Prepare basecourse.

Step 5 Apply termite poisoning if required.

Step 6 Place polythene membrane and lay reinforcing mesh.

Step 7 Pour concrete slab.

Materials:

1. Bricks or blocks
2. Sand , cement and plasticiser
3. Base gravel or metal
4. Sand topdressing
5. Polythene membrane
6. Steel mesh
7. Anchor bolts
8. Chairs and chair bases to support mesh
9. Tie wires or bag ties
10. Timber to form cavity rebate if required

Ordering Concrete

Three facts should be stated when ordering concrete: 1. *Quantity*, 2. *Strength*, 3. *Slump*. The strength should be obtained from the house plan or specifications. The slump is the plastic quality that makes concrete easy to spread. Slump is measured in millimetres and for a slab floor, the slump ordered should be 100mm – 120mm unless an Engineer specifies otherwise.

Slab Floor Preparation

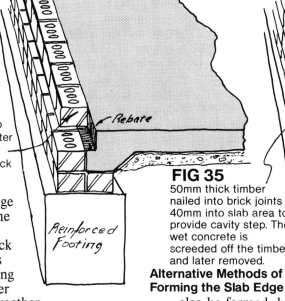

Brick course bedded in weak mortar 40mm into slab area to provide cavity step. Remove later for reuse. The wet concrete is screeded off the top of the brick course.

A step or rebate in the edge of the slab floor around the perimeter is essential if brick veneer or cavity brick walls are being used. This step prevents water crossing the cavity under the timber bottom plate during wet weather.

A simple method of forming this step is by laying a temporary brick course and the bricks can be later cleaned and reused. A bricklayer is usually on site to lay the brickwork up to slab level. Alternatively, depending on local shire requirements, this step in brick veneer work can

FIG 35

50mm thick timber nailed into brick joints 40mm into slab area to provide cavity step. The wet concrete is screeded off the timber and later removed.

Alternative Methods of Forming the Slab Edge

FIG 36

also be formed by using 125mm x 50mm or wider sized pine for ease of nailing. Nail timber on top of the base wall into mortar joints and project the timber 40mm into the slab area, thus allowing for the cavity. The wet concrete is screeded off this formwork. Wider formwork is required where doorways occur. See figure 36

Preparing Basecourse

Hold a string line on top of formwork stretched from one side of the building to the other. Make sure there is sufficient depth below this line to include both the basecourse and concrete. The thickness will be indicated on the plan. Areas that are too low, fill with gravel. Now place the basecourse which is usually 20mm gravel or metal. Topdress with sand to provide a soft bed to receive the polythene membrane. The basecourse sand should be screeded off level with a straightedge. The effort will be well rewarded by the cost saving on concrete. If the plan indicates the slab to be 100mm thick, then ensure this measurement is maintained all over the slab area.

Laying Polythene & Reinforcing Mesh

Make sure all drainage pipes and services are completed beforehand. Lay polythene ensuring a good overlap at the edges of the slab. Apply pressure sensitive tape to all joints and punctures and around pipes and fittings penetrating the polythene to prevent moisture rising. Allow 200mm laps at joins. Lay reinforcing mesh without puncturing the plastic. Ensure mesh is lapped at least one full square plus 25mm. Tie mesh together with the wire or bag ties 500mm apart along joins. Any electrical wiring for under floor heating should be laid. Bar chairs and their bases should now be placed supporting the mesh 20mm min. below the slab surface.

Pouring the Slab

It is advisable to employ an experienced team to pour the slab in one day. Do not wheelbarrow concrete directly over the mesh, support planks above the mesh to prevent the mesh from being deformed. The slab should be cured for 7 days by covering with plastic or keeping continually wet with a garden sprinkler.

Mark anchor bolt positions on boxing prior to pouring slab or tie them to slab mesh. Bolts must be installed within 15 minutes of pouring concrete and straightened as concrete firms.

On completion, make sure all concrete dribbles are washed off the face of the brickwork.

Where load bearing partitions occur, the slab is thickened directly beneath. See figure 37. The dimensions of thickenings are provided in the house plan.

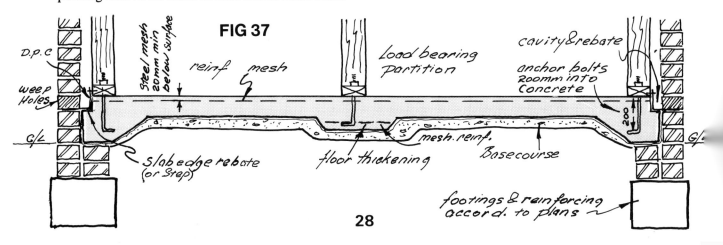

FIG 37

Slab Edge Details

Note: Where concrete slabs are abutting brick or concrete masonry around the perimeter of slab edges, a 6mm expansion strip should be laid between the two.

Brick Veneer Walls with a Slab on Ground Floor

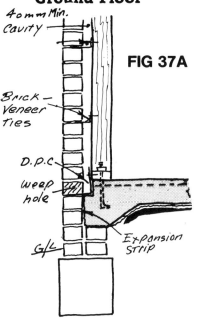

FIG 37A

Brick Veneer must have a step in the slab edge.

Brick Veneer Walls on Raft Slab Floor

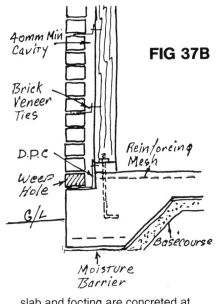

FIG 37B

slab and footing are concreted at the same time as a single entity.

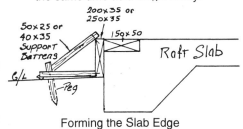

Forming the Slab Edge

Cavity Brick Walls with a Slab on Ground Floor

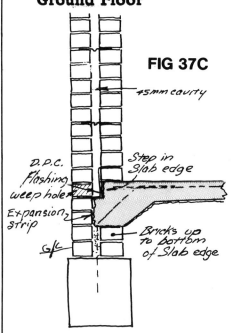

FIG 37C

Cavity brick must have a step in the slab edge. (For alternative slab edge design, see HSOB page 52.)

Weatherboard Walls with a Slab on Ground Floor

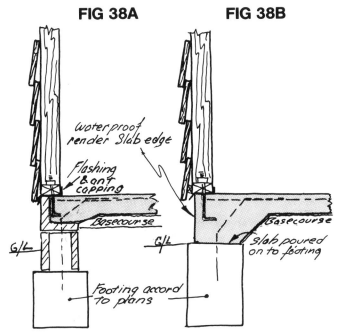

FIG 38A   FIG 38B

Hollow concrete blocks laid up to slab height and wet concrete screeded off the block edges.

Slab poured directly onto the footing.

Hollow Concrete Block Walls with a Slab on Ground Floor

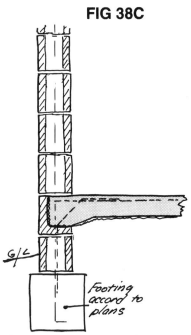

FIG 38C

Hollow concrete blocks laid up to slab height and wet concrete screeded off the block edges. See also HSOB pages 58-65.

Timber Floors & Sub Floors

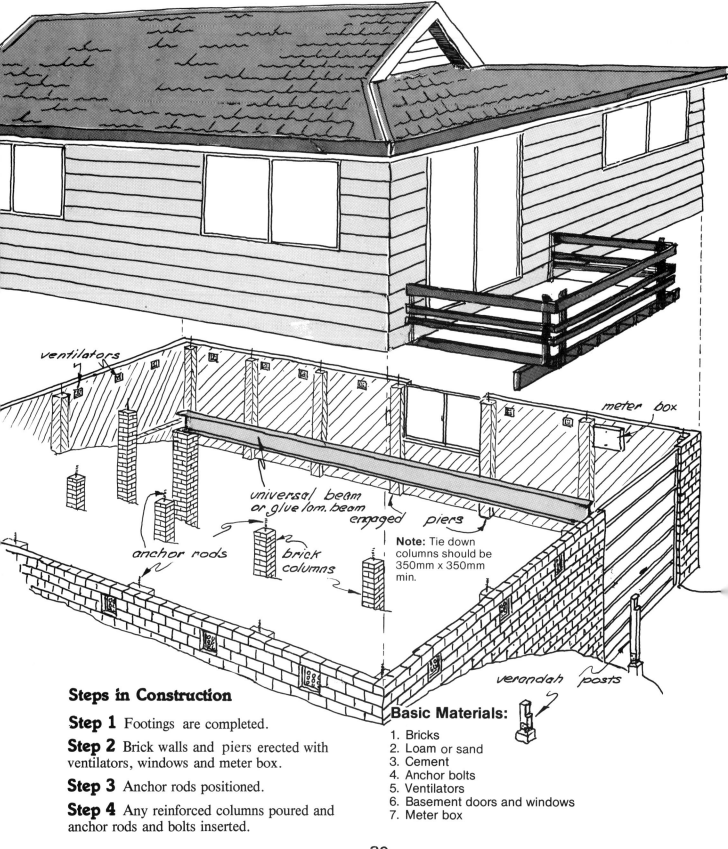

ventilators

universal beam
or glue lam. beam

engaged piers

anchor rods

brick columns

meter box

Note: Tie down columns should be 350mm x 350mm min.

verandah posts

Steps in Construction

Step 1 Footings are completed.

Step 2 Brick walls and piers erected with ventilators, windows and meter box.

Step 3 Anchor rods positioned.

Step 4 Any reinforced columns poured and anchor rods and bolts inserted.

Basic Materials:

1. Bricks
2. Loam or sand
3. Cement
4. Anchor bolts
5. Ventilators
6. Basement doors and windows
7. Meter box

30

Single Leaf Brick Bases

When single leaf masonry walls are used for basements, perimeter walls with engaged piers are built to support the bearer and to add stability to the wall. Where these walls exceed a specific height, many Councils will require an Engineer's design. Below are methods commonly used. However, the builder should consult the local Council's requirement. (See also HSOB pages 43-45)

Method A   (for walls up to 1.5m high)

The single leaf perimeter wall is built with engaged piers 230×110mm at designated centres. Also 230mm×230mm engaged piers are built to support junctions of bearers. The foundation walls are increased in thickness at their bases to 230mm thick up to 1800mm below the underside of bearers.

Method B   (for walls over 1.5m high)

For walls from 1.5m – 2.4m high
This method now required in Queensland provides superior holding down qualities. The 110mm thick wall is constructed with 350mmx 350mm engaged piers at centres determined by the spans allowed by the particular bearer used. All piers contain 1/12mm reinforcing bar taken up from the footing through the bearer and the brick core is filled with concrete grout. 110mm engaged piers are not allowed and the 230mm thick base wall to 1800mm below bearers or plates is not required.

Ventilators
Approved ventilators are positioned in walls immediately below bearers at the specified centres.

Bearers & Joists

Bearers See figures 40 & 41.

Bearers are the subfloor timbers laid on edge supporting the floor joists.

Bearer Span

The span is the distance between points of support. Bearers can be increased in size in order to increase the span and reduce the number of piers or vice versa.

Bearer Spacing

The spacing can be increased to reduce the rows of bearers required but the joist depth will have to be increased. Reducing the spacing of the bearers may mean an extra bearer and a row of piers but the joist depth will decrease resulting in less shrinkage problems.

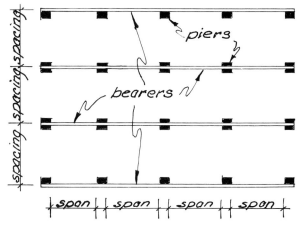

FIG 40

Joist Shrinkage

Remember a large joist can shrink up to 15mm. This type of structural movement can cause a lot of future problems. It is advisable when using large joists to buy seasoned or semi seasoned timber. (Cyprus pine has a low shrinkage factor.)

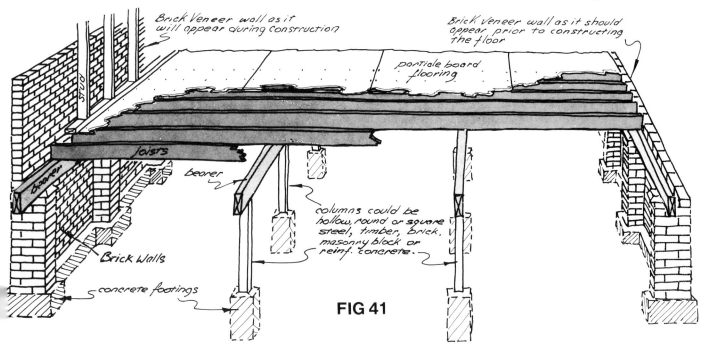

FIG 41

Laying Bearers

Bearers with serious defects such as large knots etc. should be replaced. Bearers should be laid in long lengths with the bows up and with a minimum of joins. Ensure they are seated level and firm before anchoring.

Steps to Laying Bearers

Step 1 Lay bearers on saw stools and square their ends. Prepare end joint scarfs or halvings if required.

Step 2 Mark off positions where the anchor bolts pass through the bearer and drill holes.

Step 3 Fit antcapping and DPC.

Step 4 Lay bearers in position: then nail and bolt down. When cutting joints in a bearer, ensure the 2 ends seat firmly and fit snugly together. Keep joints over the centre of supports.

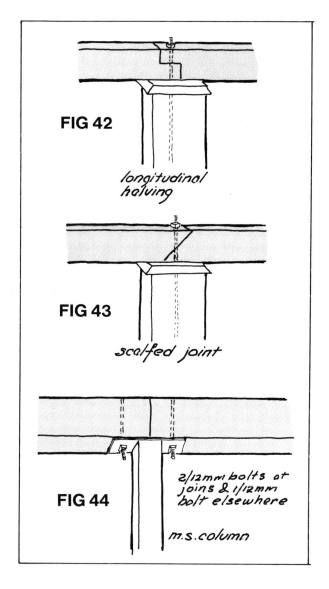

FIG 42

longitudinal halving

FIG 43

scarfed joint

FIG 44

2/12mm bolts at joins & 1/12mm bolt elsewhere

m.s.column

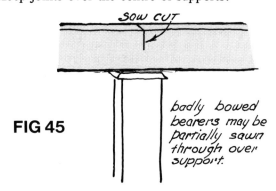

FIG 45

badly bowed bearers may be partially sawn through over support.

sow cut

Cyclone Washers for M12 bolts should be 38mmx3mm thick.

Anchoring Bearers

Anchoring methods will vary with the form of construction adopted. A house is only as secure as the anchorage provided so adhere to the specifications in case you ever have an insurance claim.
Holes are drilled slightly over the bolt diameter used but not more than 1mm in wood and 2mm in steel.

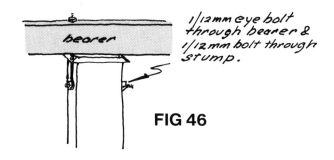

bearer

1/12mm eye bolt through bearer & 1/12mm bolt through stump.

FIG 46

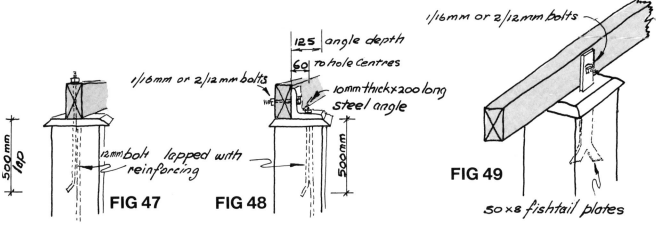

1/16mm or 2/12mm bolts

125 angle depth

60 To hole Centres

10mm thick x 200 long steel angle

12mm bolt lapped with reinforcing

500mm lap

500mm

FIG 47   **FIG 48**

FIG 49

50 x 8 fishtail plates

32

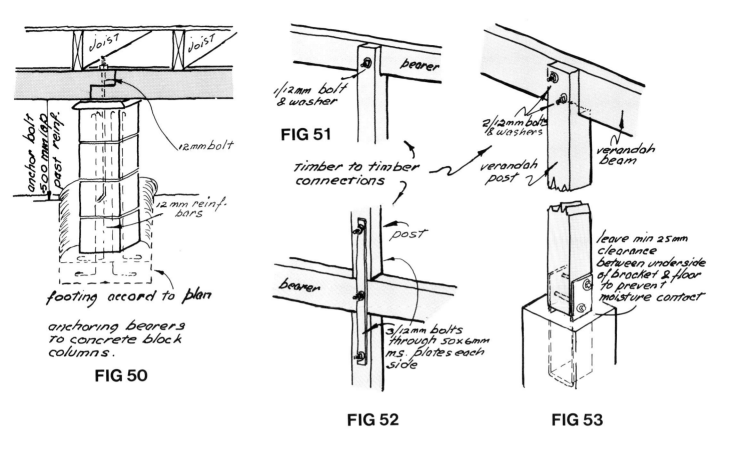

FIG 51

timber to timber connections

1/12mm bolt & washer — bearer

2/12mm bolts & washers — verandah beam

verandah post

FIG 50

joist · joist

anchor bolt 500 mm into post reinf.

12mm bolt

12 mm reinf. bars

footing accord to plan

anchoring bearers to concrete block columns.

FIG 52

post

bearer

3/12mm bolts through 50x6mm m.s. plates each side

FIG 53

leave min 25mm clearance between underside of bracket & floor to prevent moisture contact

---

Installing Beams

How to Install Beams

Prepare the same as you would for bearers using sawstools. Before lifting into position, measure the depth and check if the top edge is going to arrive at the correct height. The pier may need raising or lowering. If raising, ensure packers consist of a rotproof and incompressible material.

Type of Beam

Beams can be of steel or timber. Today much use is being made of laminated timber beams. The advantages are their lighter weight, ease of fixing, drilling and cutting plus their aesthetic

appearance. Steel girders attract rust and often need to be lined or painted but are essential where head room is limited.

> When using steel beams, ensure that all bolt holes have been predrilled and check that the beam is straight. If it contains an even bow throughout its length, ensure the bow remains on top when in position.

FIG 54

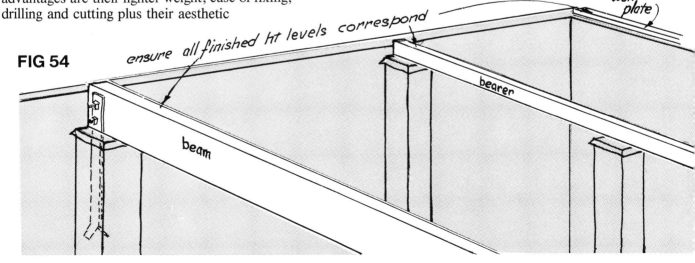

ensure all finished ht levels correspond

wall plate

bearer

beam

Floor Joists

Floor joists are regularly spaced members supporting the flooring. Their dimensions and spacings are given on the plan and specifications. They are normally from 38mm-50mm thick and from 75mm-300mm deep. Their top edges must be level throughout. Where joins occur, they must be over a support.

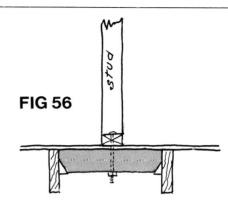

FIG 56

Where a roof load is concentrated on a stud, provide a solid bridging below the stud between the joists.

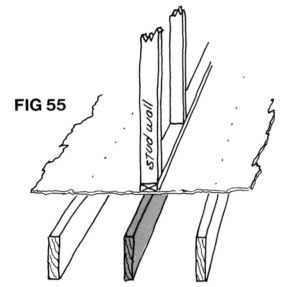

FIG 55

Provide a joist under load bearing partitions or where the load is concentrated at one or more points along the partition, use solid bridging directly beneath the points of loading as in figure 56.

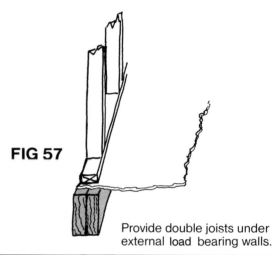

FIG 57

Provide double joists under external load bearing walls.

Below are joist connections sometimes required when nominal nailing is insufficient.

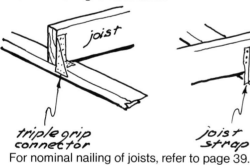

triple grip connector

joist strap

For nominal nailing of joists, refer to page 39.

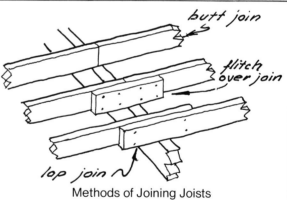

butt join

flitch over join

lap join

Methods of Joining Joists

Connecting Joists to Steel Beams

FIG 58

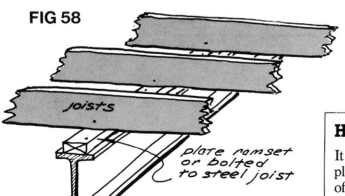

joists

plate ramset or bolted to steel joist

Hint

It is a good timesaver on the job if beforehand a plan is drawn to large scale of the proposed layout of the joists. This will also enable you to purchase the correct quantity of joists.

Platform Floors

Floor Laying Methods

Two methods of laying floors may be used with different joist application.
First Method

Platform Flooring (Most Commonly Used Today)

This refers to flooring which is laid as a continuous membrane over the whole house area with walls being constructed on top of the floor. When wet weather prevails during construction, holes are bored through the floor next to the bottom plates to prevent water ponding. When particle board is used, a joist must be located directly beneath all load bearing walls and partitions parallel to the joists and a pair of joists positioned beneath external walls parallel to the joists. See figure 60. All joists may be butt jointed as in figure 60. Where structural flooring other than particle board is used, a pair of joists must be provided below external load bearing walls parallel to joists. However, all other joists may be laid without reference to the position of walls or partitions whether load bearing or non-load bearing. However, on the lower story of a 2-storey house, joists must be positioned directly beneath all load bearing walls and partitions parallel to the joists.

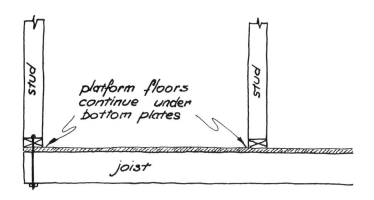

FIG 59

Load Bearing Walls and Partitions

These support ceiling and roof loads. The studs may be required to be increased in dimension. Check local code requirements.

A non load bearing partition carries no roof or floor loads but may support ceiling only.

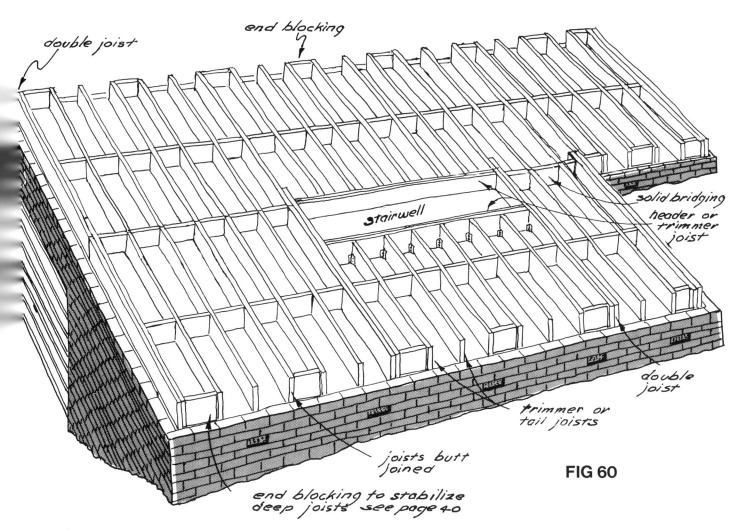

FIG 60

Cut In Floors

Cut in Floors (or Fitted Floors)

Cut in floors are seldom applied today to new house construction. However, an understanding of the method is essential for those engaged in additions and alterations to older homes where floors have been cut in.

The floor is laid after walls and partitions have been erected. They are cut in to fit beside the bottom plates as described in figure 64. Structural particle board, T&G strip flooring or similar acceptable to the code may be used. A pair of joists is required under all walls and partitions parallel to joists. There must be a 12mm minimum bearing on the joists beside the wall bottom plates for nailing the flooring. See figure 62.

Joists should be lapped 300mm or butt joined with a flitch nailed to the side of joists as in figure 61. Keep flitch 25mm below top edges. Where support is required along the edge of the double joists, a packer is nailed at 600mm centres between the joists and to the depth of the joists but 12mm below the surface to allow for shrinkage. see fig. 64

> **Note –** Where deep joists require end and intermediate stiffening, either solid bridging or herringbone strutting may be used (regardless of which type has been depicted in the illustration). Keep top edges of bridging or strutting 12mm below joist tops. See also page 40.

FIG 61

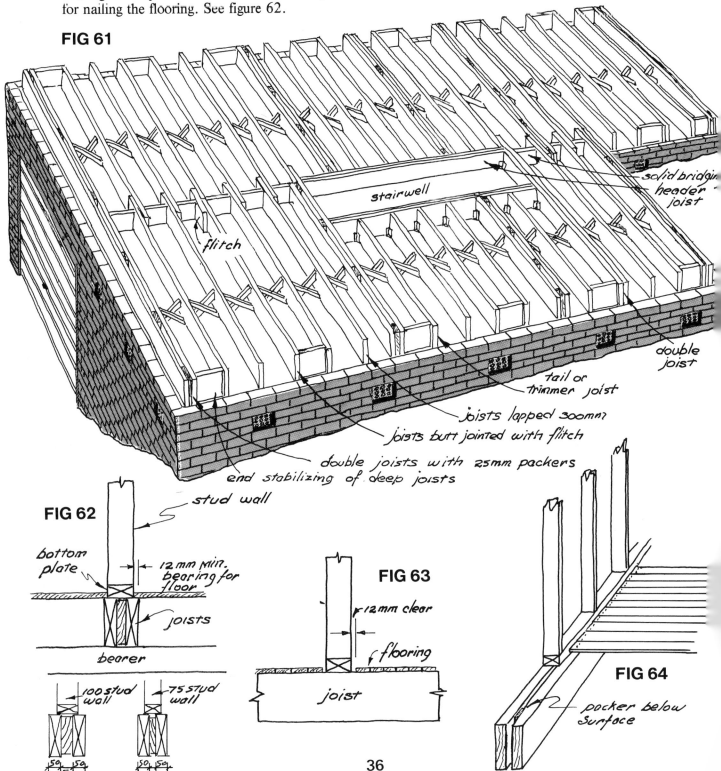

FIG 62

FIG 63

FIG 64

Setting Out Floor Joists

(For Platform or Cut in Floors)

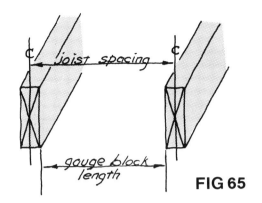

FIG 65

The following is a simple, quick and accurate method of setting out joist positions. All joist positions should be marked on the bearers, wall plates and beams prior to loading the joists. A gauge block should be cut out of stock the thickness of which corresponds to that of the joists being used. For example, a 100mm x 50mm or 75mm x 50mm for 50mm thick joists and 100mm x 38mm for 38mm thick joists. Then cut to length as described in figure 65.

Because the thickness of the gauge block corresponds with the joist thickness, a line can be drawn down either side to show the joist position. An 'X' should be placed inside the lines to help clarify the joist position.

FIG 66A

To indicate the joist, hold gauge block square and parallel with the bearer and mark the joist spacing as in figure 66A. To achieve accurate spacings, keep pencil point tight against the gauge. To show the line at the opposite side of the joist, simply use the gauge on its edge as in figure 66B.

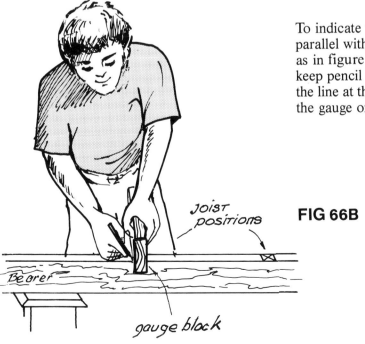

FIG 66B

Setting Out Floor Joists Cont.

Steps to Laying Joists

Step 1 Mark out positions of joists on bearers.

Step 2 Secure the joists in position. Double and trimmer joists first: then the remaining joists.

Step 3 Level off the top edges of the joists.

Step 4 Attach any solid bridging or herringbone strutting and nogging.

How to Mark Joist Positions

Step 1 From the plan, find and indicate the positions of the external and internal walls that run parallel with the joists, marking them on the outside bearers and plates using light pencil lines. If using structural flooring other than particle board, then joists are not required under internal partitions unless those partitions support an upper floor.

Step 2 Now place the joist position marks over these proposed wall positions including any double joists. If there is a trimmed stairwell running parallel with the joists, indicate these trimmer joists now.

Step 3 Mark the position of joists supporting the edge of any sheet flooring joins.

Step 4 Work from one end and using the gauge as previously described, mark off the intermediate joists. You will find when you arrive at a partition or joist supporting a sheet flooring join that the spacing is shorter than the normal guage length: simply centralize the last joist spacings or leave the last spacing shorter.

Step 5 Repeat these joist positions on to the opposite side of the building. Then, holding a chalk line on these marks across the building, spring corresponding marks on to the intermediate bearers.

Ensure joists do not cross the path of waste pipes such as where goosenecks arrive below bath and shower or W.C. outlets.

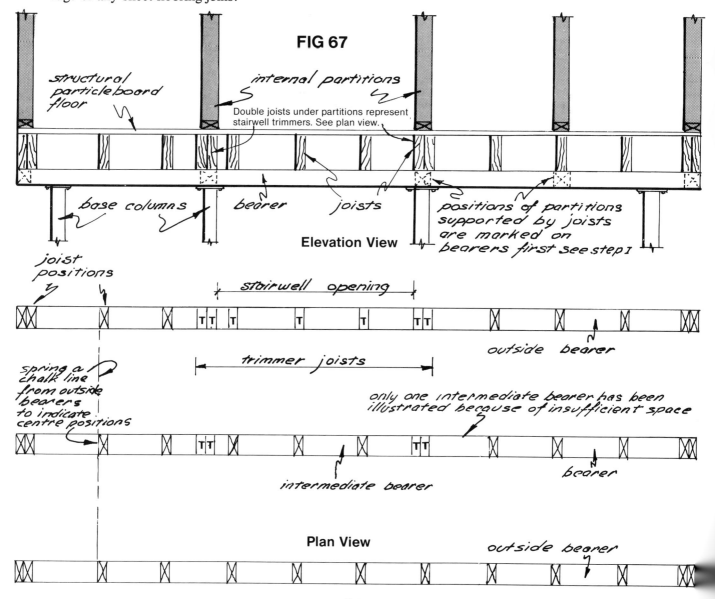

FIG 67

structural particleboard floor

internal partitions

Double joists under partitions represent stairwell trimmers. See plan view.

base columns   bearer   joists   positions of partitions supported by joists are marked on bearers first see step 1

Elevation View

joist positions

stairwell opening

trimmer joists

outside bearer

spring a chalk line from outside bearers to indicate centre positions

only one intermediate bearer has been illustrated because of insufficient space

intermediate bearer

bearer

Plan View

outside bearer

outside bearer

Laying Floor Joists

Laying Joists

Step 1 Joists can now have their ends squared and cut to length. This procedure can be undertaken on sawstools at ground level. When the joists are later laid in their final positions, their top edges should be on the same level plane. If the joists have been brought to the site sized (that is all dressed to the same depth), then continue with step 2. However, when rough sawn (or unsized   their bearing points will have to be gauged down to a uniform depth. See figure 68.

How to Gauge Joists to Size

Measure the depth of the narrowest joists and set your carpenter's combination square to this depth. Using the square as a gauge, mark the ends of each joist with a carpenter's pencil, to the bearer or plate width. Check out the excess. See figure 68. This waste could be from 2mm-6mm. Remember when marking, to gauge down from the bowed or top edges of the joists.

Step 2 Now join together all of the double joists with packing pieces in place (if they are required) keeping the bowed edges uppermost. Working from one end and again keeping the bowed edges uppermost proceed to skewnail the ends to the bearers. If nails are splitting the joists, drill holes 4/5th the Dia.of the nails being used. When nails split joist ends, they remain insecure. The little effort of drilling is essential. Specifications may require joists to be secured using straps or triplegrips.

Step 3 Joist tops are now checked for any bumps or for joists bowed above surrounding joists. These high spots are removed with the electric plane. See figure 70

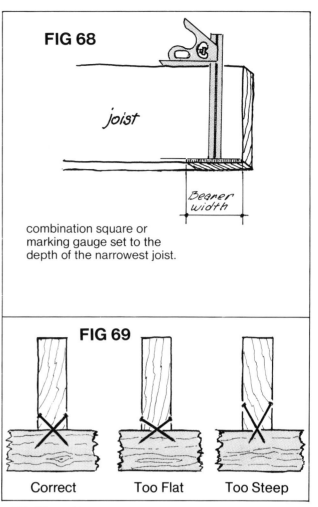

FIG 68

joist

Bearer width

combination square or marking gauge set to the depth of the narrowest joist.

FIG 69

Correct   Too Flat   Too Steep

Nailing Joists

Joists are skewnailed to the plates and bearers with 2/75mm nails at a 45 degree angle as shown in figure 69.

Diameter of Nails

The thickest nail that can be driven without significant splitting of the timber is taken as the acceptable diameter.

Nails should penetrate their receiving member 10 dia. into side grain and 15 dia. into end grain.

Using a straightedge, check the tops of the joists for any high spot or for any joists bowed above those surrounding it. Remove these high spots and bows using an electric planer.

FIG 70

bearer

Solid Bridging

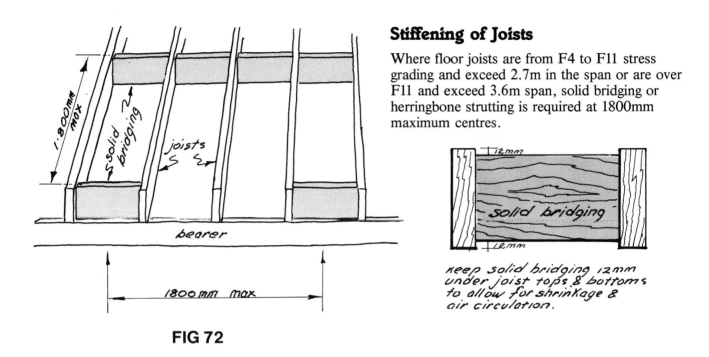

FIG 72

Stiffening of Joists

Where floor joists are from F4 to F11 stress grading and exceed 2.7m in the span or are over F11 and exceed 3.6m span, solid bridging or herringbone strutting is required at 1800mm maximum centres.

keep solid bridging 12mm under joist tops & bottoms to allow for shrinkage & air circulation.

Herringbone Strutting

Herringbone strutting is usually cut out of 50mm x 38mm or 50mm x 50mm timber.

How to Find the Length and Bevel of Herringbone Struts.

Step 1 Spring a chalk line across the joist tops near the point where the joists are secured and check that the pair of joists are sitting plumb off the bearer or wall plate to ensure accuracy.

Step 2 Then supposing the joists are 250mm deep, spring another line 225mm away from the first line. This represents the depth of the strut. The 25mm discrepancy allows 12mm shrinkage for top and bottom of joists.

Step 3 Hold a piece of strutting material on these chalk lines. With a pencil, mark the underside of the strut to the line of the joists. If the joists are evenly spaced, the first strut can be used as a pattern for the remainder.

Securing the Struts

Struts should be secured to a chalk line sprung through the joist tops. To ensure the struts are in plumb alignment, a plumb line should be drawn on the face of each joist. Ensure that their top and bottom points are kept 12mm inside the top and bottom edges of the joists.

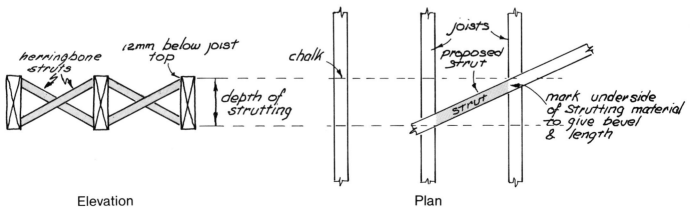

Elevation   Plan

Cantilevered Joists

Cantilevering of floor members enables the floor area or patio to be larger than the base or foundation it rests on. Cantilevered joists must be adequately anchored to their supporting header member or beam. Purpose made saddles are appropriate. The supporting joists (sometimes called a header) member can be a double joist or a laminated beam. Care should be taken that this member is sufficiently anchored. In some canterlever situations, the services of a structural engineer will be required to design members, saddles and fixings.

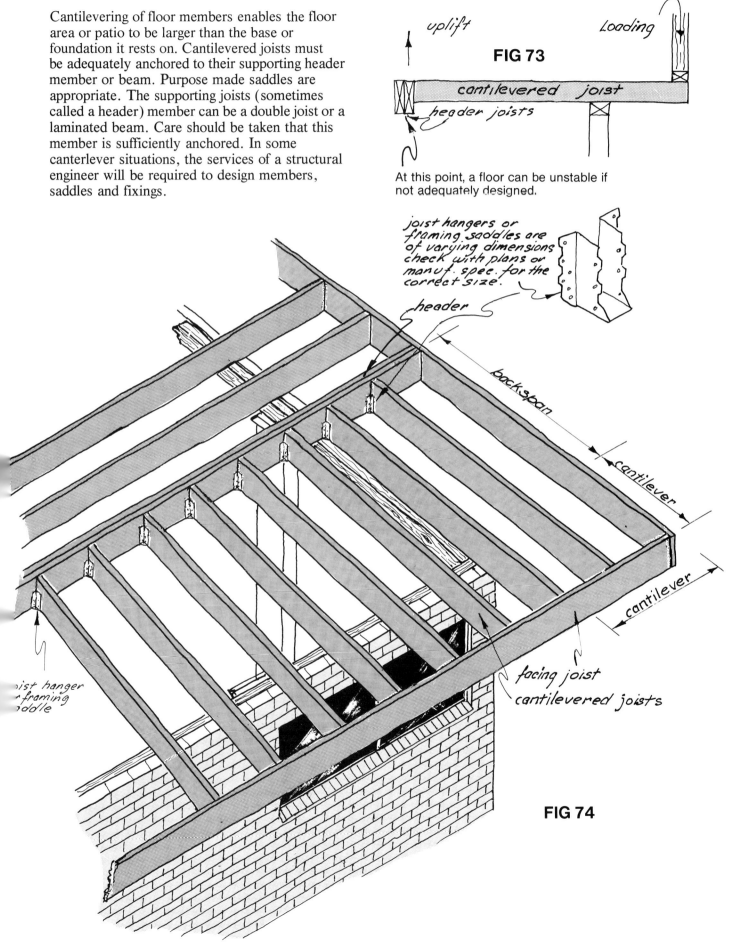

uplift

Loading

FIG 73

cantilevered joist

header joists

At this point, a floor can be unstable if not adequately designed.

joist hangers or framing saddles are of varying dimensions check with plans or manuf. spec. for the correct size.

header

backspan

cantilever

cantilever

joist hanger or framing saddle

facing joist

cantilevered joists

FIG 74

Cantilevered Joists Cont.

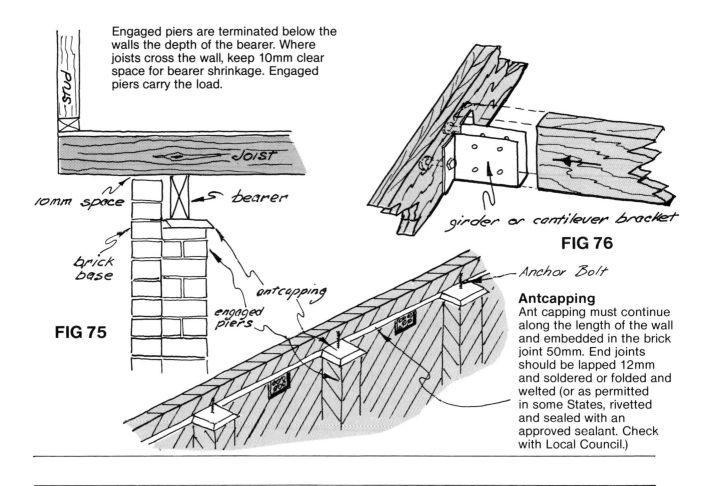

Engaged piers are terminated below the walls the depth of the bearer. Where joists cross the wall, keep 10mm clear space for bearer shrinkage. Engaged piers carry the load.

STUD

Joist

10mm space

bearer

brick base

antcapping

engaged piers

FIG 75

girder or cantilever bracket

FIG 76

Anchor Bolt

Antcapping

Ant capping must continue along the length of the wall and embedded in the brick joint 50mm. End joints should be lapped 12mm and soldered or folded and welted (or as permitted in some States, rivetted and sealed with an approved sealant. Check with Local Council.)

Stairwell Trimmer Joists

Stairwell Trimmer Joists

For stairwells or openings in floors up to 1m, the trimmer joists can remain the same size as the common joists. However, for openings from 1m-3m, the trimmer thickness is increased by 1/3rd for every 300mm over 1m in length.

stairwell opening

stairwell opening

stairwell

trimmer joist thickness

curtailed joist

FIG 77

Sheet Flooring

Sheet Flooring

If using the platform method, when sheet flooring arrives on the job, have it offloaded directly on to the floor joists but not in one stack. This procedure saves double handling. Prior to sheets arriving, make sure all joists and noggs are in place and the joist surface has been checked for any high spots

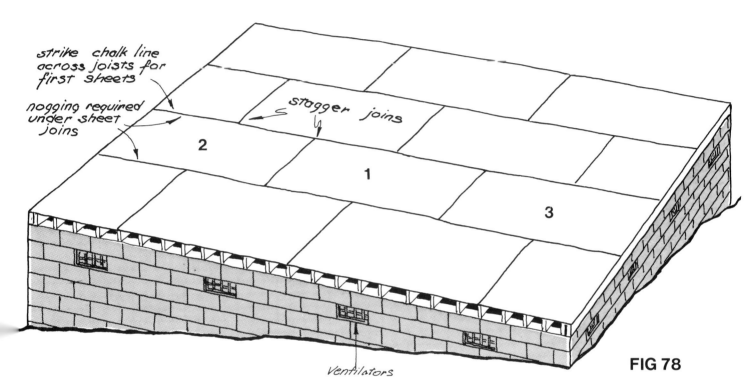

strike chalk line across joists for first sheets

nogging required under sheet joins

stagger joins

2

1

3

Ventilators

FIG 78

How to Lay Sheet Flooring

Step 1 A chalk line is struck down the centre of the building measured in from one side in even sheet modules. The opposite side sheets may overhang. These can be trimmed off after all the sheets have been laid. The trimmed off pieces may be used to fill in any narrow spaces.

Step 2 Begin laying the sheets from the centre line out and only tack the corners temporarily. Make sure the joins are tight. If a sheet refuses to close, carefully plane the offending edge. If using T&G sheets, make sure the grooves are clear of sawdust.

Step 3 For a nailing guide, spring a chalk line across the floor indicating the centre of all joists. Nail from the centre of the sheets out towards the edges using nails and nail spacings recommended by the Manufacturer. If the sheets are to be glued down as well, follow the directions set out by the Manufacturer.

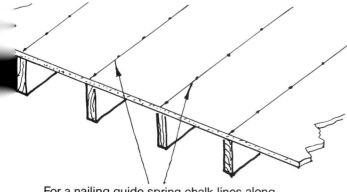

For a nailing guide spring chalk lines along the centre line of each joist.

Warning – The structural strength of particle board flooring will deteriorate if exposed to the weather longer than recommended by the Manufacturer.

T&G Flooring

T&G flooring is popular because Australian hardwood and cyprus pine offer an attractive and colourful finish especially when surfaced with polyurethene and epoxy coatings. The floor is easily cared for and can be an initial cost saving. It is mainly suitable for warmer areas.

Nails should be driven at a slight angle to give increased holding power. This rule should apply to almost all nailing in carpentering.

FIG 79

Steps to Laying T&G Flooring

Step 1 Spring a chalk line down the centre of the building across the joists and tack the first board to the edge of this line. When straightened, drive the nails home.

Step 2 Lay out 4 or 5 rows of boards against the first board and apply floor cramps. Fit a length of straight 75mm x 50mm timber between the floor cramps and T&G boards to prevent bruising. Make sure the boards are tight before nailing off. When cramping, move the cramps to a different pair of joists each time. This contributes to keeping the boards straight.

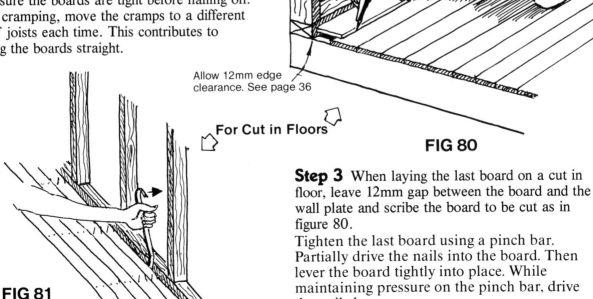

Allow 12mm edge clearance. See page 36

For Cut in Floors

FIG 80

FIG 81

Step 3 When laying the last board on a cut in floor, leave 12mm gap between the board and the wall plate and scribe the board to be cut as in figure 80.

Tighten the last board using a pinch bar. Partially drive the nails into the board. Then lever the board tightly into place. While maintaining pressure on the pinch bar, drive the nails home.

4

Wall Framing

Timber for House Framing (For Use in Subfloor, Walls and Roof)

The structural strength of timber is identified by the stress grading code. The code is a number preceded by the letter "F" and ranges between F4 and F22. The higher the number, the stronger the timber. The stress grading can also be identified by the appropriate colour being marked on the timber.

Stress Grading	Colour Coding
F 4	Red
F 5	Black
F 7	Blue
F 8	Green
F11	Purple
F14	Orange
F17	Yellow
F22	White

Listed below are actual timber framing sizes nominated for hardwood and cyprus as well as radiata. Some of these sizes may have to be ordered in advance. All timber is purchased in 300mm increments.

Hardwood & Cyprus Pine

75x38	75x50	275x50	225x 75
100x38	100x50	300x50	250x 75
125x38	125x50	75x75	275x 75
150x38	150x50	100x75	300x 75
175x38	175x50	125x75	100x100
200x38	200x50	150x75	125x100
225x38	225x50	175x75	150x100
250x38	250x50	200x75	125x125

Radiata Pine

70x35	70x45	70x70	90x90
90x35	90x45	90x70	
120x35	120x45	120x70	
140x35	140x45	140x70	
190x35	190x45	190x70	
240x35	240x45	240x70	
290x35	290x45	290x70	

Timber Shrinkage

Shrinkage of timber can cause enormous problems in the months following the completion of the house. Damage can be evident in cracked wallboards and gaps appearing around mouldings. Where brick veneer is used, damage can occur to brick sills and soffits. To avoid this, see page 93. A large proportion of shrinkage can be avoided if the depth of the floor joists or/and bearers can be reduced. See page 31. (Also see HSOB pages 30-31)

Wall Framing

Timber wall frames consist of vertical and horizontal timbers regularly spaced to provide a nailing base for attaching the interior and exterior wall linings. Openings are provided within the frame to receive windows and doors. The top of the frame supports the roof. Internal walls are referred to as partitions. Frames supporting the roof and ceiling loads are termed load bearing walls or partitions. Wall frames are usually constructed after the floor has been laid although the reverse is acceptable. See pages 35 and 36. They are normally assembled on the floor and then raised to their vertical positions. However, they can be built stud by stud insitu.

How to Assemble Insitu: The bottom plate is fixed all round the perimeter: corner and intersection studs added, plumbed and braced: the top plate is secured and finally, intermediate studs inserted one at a time.

Of the two, this method is better suited to special situations, where, for example, the top plate slopes on a rake (called a raking plate: also where raising a floor assembled frame would prove too awkward.

Framing can be carried out in three ways.

They are:-
1. Factory precut and prenailed.
2. Factory precut and assembled on site.
3. Wholly cut out and assembled on site.

They should be individually considered and costed. Where time is at a premium, it may be advisable to opt for the more expensive precut and prenailed frame. The following pages, however, will assist those wishing to cut and nail their own frames.

Wall Member Identification

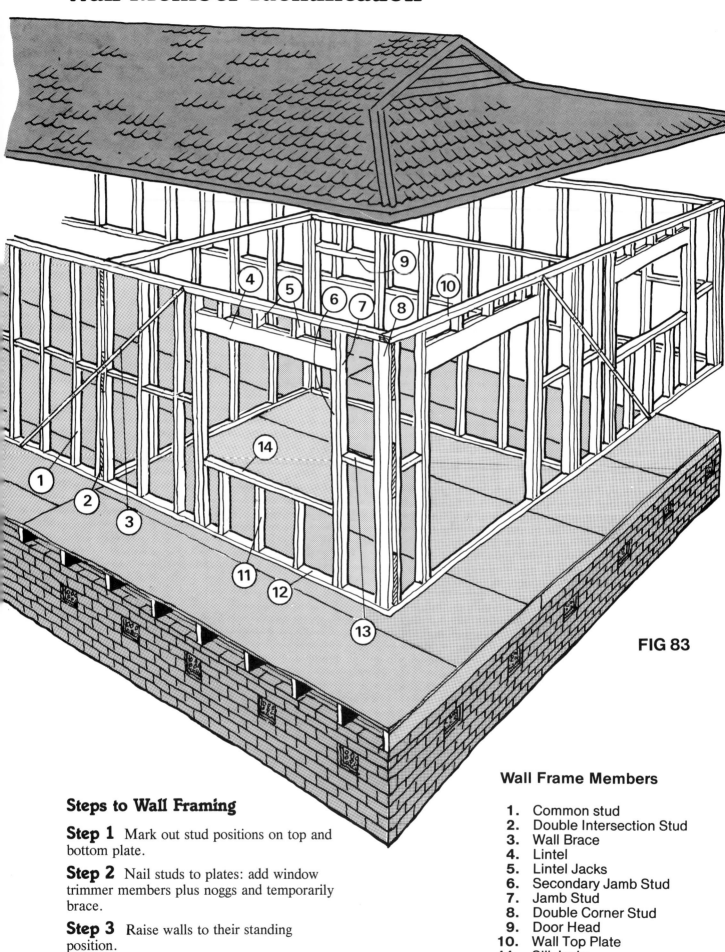

FIG 83

Steps to Wall Framing

Step 1 Mark out stud positions on top and bottom plate.

Step 2 Nail studs to plates: add window trimmer members plus noggs and temporarily brace.

Step 3 Raise walls to their standing position.

Step 4 Straighten bottom plate and secure in position. Plumb corners and brace: then straighten the top plates and brace.

Wall Frame Members

1.   Common stud
2.   Double Intersection Stud
3.   Wall Brace
4.   Lintel
5.   Lintel Jacks
6.   Secondary Jamb Stud
7.   Jamb Stud
8.   Double Corner Stud
9.   Door Head
10. Wall Top Plate
11. Sill Jacks
12. Wall Bottom Plate
13. Noggs
14. Sill Trimmer

46

Stud Positioning

Standard Nogg Length See figure 84

To determine standard nogg length, mark stud centres on a length of plate material. Then mark off one stud thickness from one centre line. The remaining space to the opposite centre line will be standard nogg length. Use this first nogg as a pattern for marking off stud positions and for cutting the remaining standard noggs.

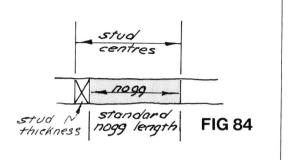

FIG 84

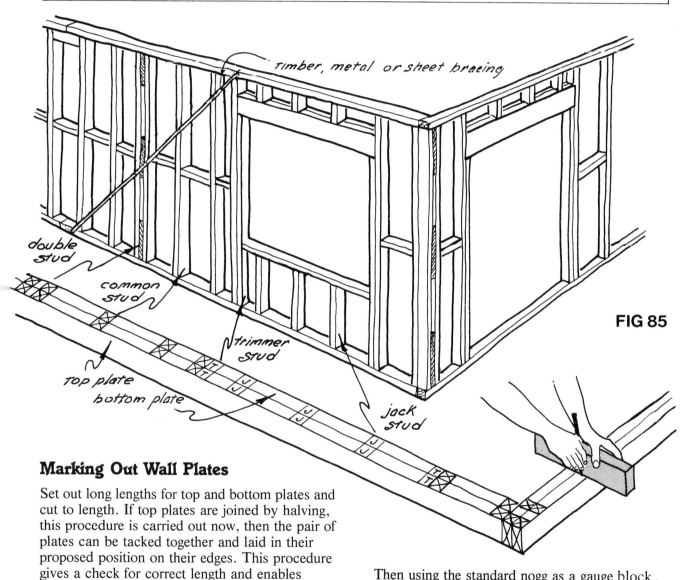

FIG 85

Marking Out Wall Plates

Set out long lengths for top and bottom plates and cut to length. If top plates are joined by halving, this procedure is carried out now, then the pair of plates can be tacked together and laid in their proposed position on their edges. This procedure gives a check for correct length and enables speedy location of plates.

Procedure for Marking Stud Positions

Step 1 First mark the positions of corner studs: then partition intersection studs.

Step 2 Window and door trimmer stud locations are now indicated. If there are any studs supporting exposed beams, mark these positions now.

Step 3 Some wall linings require a stud to support a vertical sheet join. Position these now.

Then using the standard nogg as a gauge block, mark off all the remaining common stud positions. This is done in the same manner as described for indicating joist positions as in figures 66A & 66B, page 37. Whenever one of the previously marked stud positions is arrived at, there will be an odd spacing smaller than the standard nogg. It is standard practice to disregard this and not attempt to equalize the stud positions. Noggs are later cut to fit all these odd spaces.

Step 4 Roof trusses and ceiling joist positions can also be marked at this stage on the top side of the top plate. This could be postponed until after the frame is erected.

Joining Wall Plates

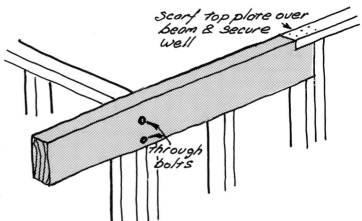

Cantilevered Beam & Top Plate Connection

Joining Plates

Top plate joints may be halved and lapped or joined by nail plates or straps. If halving is used, avoid end splitting. Ensure the top plate joins do not arrive above openings. The top plate joints must be supported by a nogg directly underneath as in figure 87A or by a stud in figure 87B. Bottom plates are butt joined.

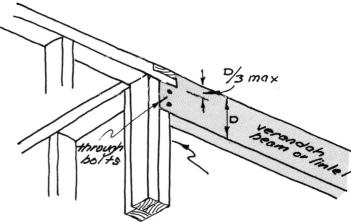

Cross sectional size of supporting stud should not be less than that required for a stud supporting a lintel in an opening with a similar span.

Verandah Beam or Lintel & Top Plate Connection

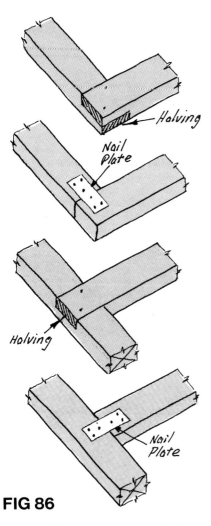

FIG 86

Typical Top Plate Jointing Methods

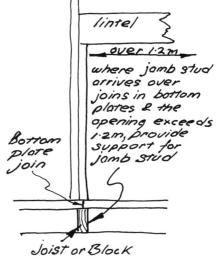

FIG 87A   **FIG 87B**

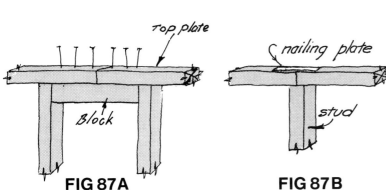

Longitudinal Joins in Top Wall Plates

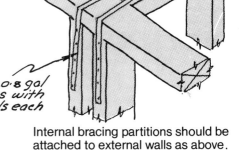

Internal bracing partitions should be attached to external walls as above. (bracing partitions are those containing a brace).

48

Stud and Jack Stud Lengths

Preparing Studs

Studs are squared and trimmed to their respective
lengths. Keep straight and bowed studs in
separate stacks arranged closely and neat but
away from the sun and wind if possible. Use as
soon as possible after cutting. When the standard
studs are all cut, continue cutting the remaining
trimmer studs, then sill and jack studs. Lastly, cut
the standard noggs: then the smaller odd shaped
noggs. Notice the procedure is to cut from the
longest stud component down to the smallest
nogg. This method utilizes offcuts. Badly bowed
lengths can be cut into shorter sizes. Keep straight
timber for trimmer studs and window sills.
Below is an example of how to arrive at the
correct stud length. These measurements will vary
with the various material sizes used. However, the
basic method of arriving at the stud length remains
the same.

Example:

To find the Stud Length for the Typical Situation
in Figure 88

Take ceiling height	2.400
Add ceiling thickness	12
	2.412
Deduct top and bottom plates thickness of 50mm each	100
	2.312
Add 10mm as a clearance for fitting wall sheets	10
Stud Length =	2.322mm

*If a cut in floor or lowered ceiling battens are
used, the stud length is adjusted accordingly.*

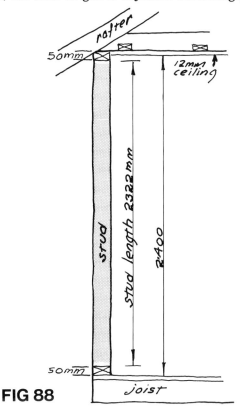

FIG 88

Studs

The spacing and dimensions of studs is
determined by the load they will carry and the
wall linings they will be supporting. These
dimensions are shown on the plans and
specifications.

The Story Rod

After cutting the common studs, make a story rod
to establish trimmer, lintel and sill jack stud
lengths. Take a straight stud and mark all lintels
and sill positions accurately. Write on each their
respective room positions. All four sides of the
rod can be used. Lintels as a rule, continue at the
same height throughout. Usually if sliding
aluminium doors are used, this head height will be
used as the governing height for all lintels. Add a
12mm gap between joinery and timber lintel for
shrinkage. Mark off the bottom and top sides of
each lintel. The space remaining above the lintel is
the *lintel jack stud length.* Now establish sill
heights by measuring down from the bottom of the
lintel plus the 12mm shrinkage allowance and a
further 4mm for levelling up of windows later.
Mark top and bottom sides of sill trimmer. The
remaining space below the sill will be *sill jack
lengths.* Studs supporting lintels are now
measured from the bottom side of lintels to the
bottom of the story rod.

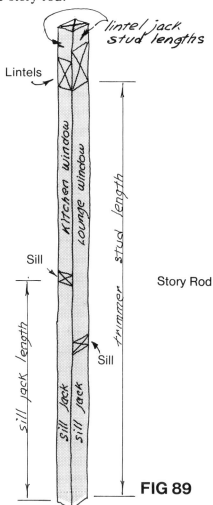

FIG 89

Cutting Studs

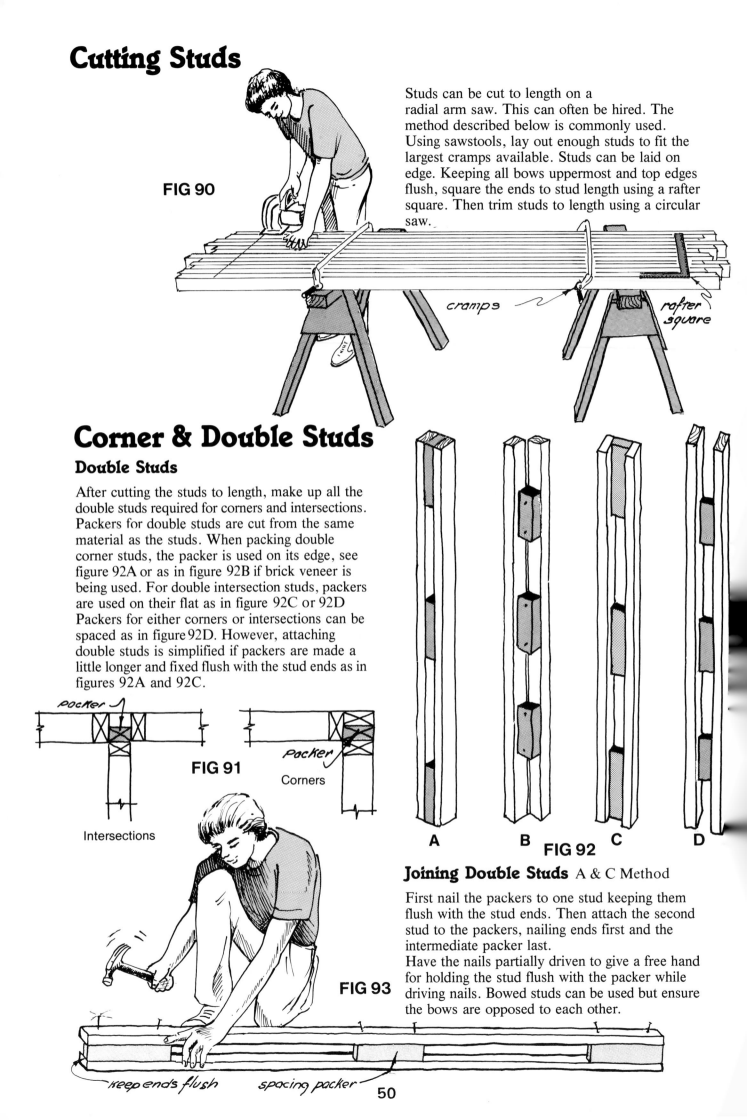

FIG 90

Studs can be cut to length on a radial arm saw. This can often be hired. The method described below is commonly used. Using sawstools, lay out enough studs to fit the largest cramps available. Studs can be laid on edge. Keeping all bows uppermost and top edges flush, square the ends to stud length using a rafter square. Then trim studs to length using a circular saw.

cramps

rafter square

Corner & Double Studs

Double Studs

After cutting the studs to length, make up all the double studs required for corners and intersections. Packers for double studs are cut from the same material as the studs. When packing double corner studs, the packer is used on its edge, see figure 92A or as in figure 92B if brick veneer is being used. For double intersection studs, packers are used on their flat as in figure 92C or 92D Packers for either corners or intersections can be spaced as in figure 92D. However, attaching double studs is simplified if packers are made a little longer and fixed flush with the stud ends as in figures 92A and 92C.

packer

FIG 91

packer

Corners

Intersections

A   **B**   **FIG 92**   **C**   **D**

Joining Double Studs A & C Method

First nail the packers to one stud keeping them flush with the stud ends. Then attach the second stud to the packers, nailing ends first and the intermediate packer last.

Have the nails partially driven to give a free hand for holding the stud flush with the packer while driving nails. Bowed studs can be used but ensure the bows are opposed to each other.

FIG 93

keep ends flush   *spacing packer*

50

Wall Frame Assembly

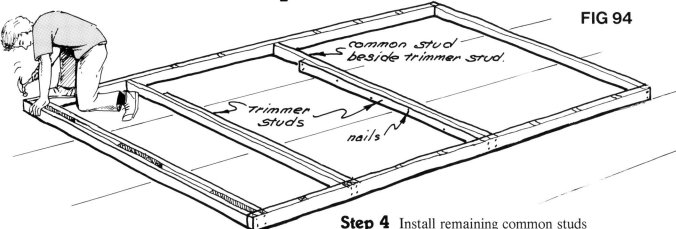

FIG 94

common stud beside trimmer stud.

Trimmer studs

nails

How to Assemble Wall Frames

Step 1 Lay out plates in line with a chalk line as a guide for keeping the frame approximately square. Lay the bottom plate in proximity to its proposed erected position to avoid unnecessary handling of the assembled frame later.

Step 2 Install studs near the end of the frame first: then any trimmer and intersection studs.

Step 3 Fit lintels, sills and jack studs

Step 4 Install remaining common studs

Step 5 Fit noggs in position

Step 6 Square frame and fit bracing

Hint

When laying out frames preparatory to nailing, check by sight that the frame is approximately square before driving any nails home. If a frame is assembled noticeably out of square, it may take quite a bit of heaving and shoving to rectify later.

Lintels

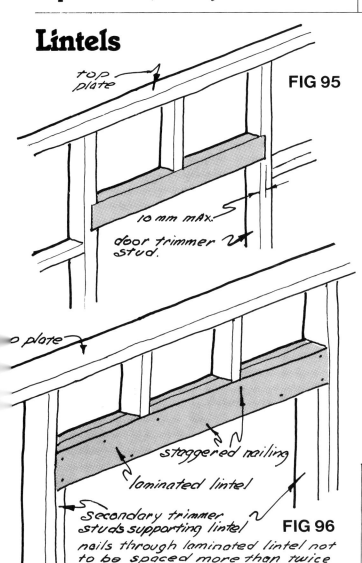

FIG 95

top plate

10 mm mAx.

door trimmer stud.

o plate

staggered nailing

laminated lintel

secondary trimmer studs supporting lintel   **FIG 96**

nails through laminated lintel not to be spaced more than twice lintel depth apart.

Laminated Lintel

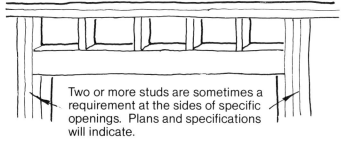

Two or more studs are sometimes a requirement at the sides of specific openings. Plans and specifications will indicate.

Support of Lintels

More than one stud may be required to support each end of lintels; depending on stud height; effective roof length; and proposed roof load. Check these requirements with the specifications.

Lintels

Lintels support the roof and ceiling above openings. Lintels housed into studs (figure 95) can only be used for openings up to 1200mm wide. For all others, use secondary jamb studs to rest the lintel on. When lintels are required to be stud width in 75mm walls, solid one piece lintels can be used. Where the stud width is 90-100mm, it is preferable to use 2 lintels nailed together and referred to as a 'laminated lintel'. See figure 96

Hint

Keep lintel bows facing outside and ensure sides of lintels, especially one piece lintels, are not badly bowed as this could create difficulties when lining and finishing the interior.
It is preferable for lintels over 175mm deep to be seasoned.

Nogging (Dwangs)

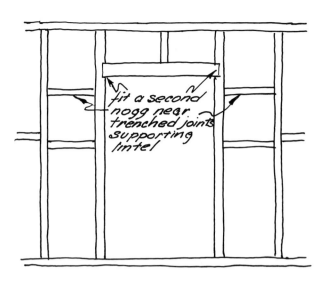

Nogging

One row of nogging is required at 1350mm maximum centres to reduce stud twisting and to stiffen the centre of the frames. In some cases, this will also provide a fixing base for wall lining joins. If vertical board lining is being applied to the external surface, then attach 3 rows of noggs equally spaced in 2.4m high walls or as directed in the Manufacturer's specifications. Nogging is usually cut from the same stock as studs. Noggs, when fixed in a staggered pattern, are easier to nail in place. When they are used for joining sheets on, they must be kept in line. If gyprock sheets are laid horizontally, noggs must be kept away from the proposed horizontal joint.

How to Install Noggs

Spring a chalk line across studs as a nailing guide. Use 4 nails to each nogg: 2 at each end. Leave end noggs out of the frame until walls have been erected, plumbed and straightened. Leave the upper nails out of noggs where it is suspected bracing may cross. This will save damage to saw teeth when cutting rebate for braces.

Sill Jacks

To obtain jack positions on sills, hold sill against the bottom plate jack stud positions and simply transfer marks across. See figure 97A

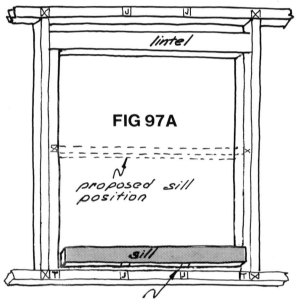

FIG 97A

Transferring sill jack positions from the bottom plate to sill

FIG 97B

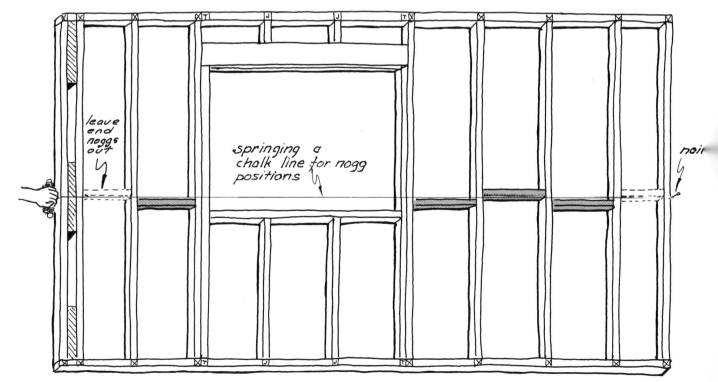

Notching Trenching & Drilling Studs

Holes drilled for services (pipes or cables) should not be larger than 1/4 of the depth of the stud and should be located inside the middle third of the stud depth. Slotting and trenching of studs for bracing should not exceed 20mm. Some situations will require the stud to be increased in depth to permit cut in bracing.

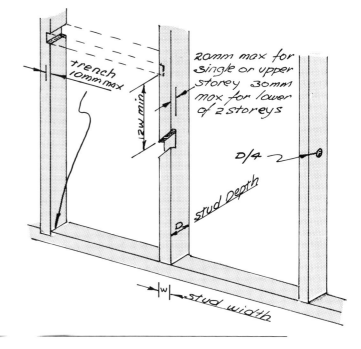

Bracing Wall Frames

Bracing is required at specified positions across the length and width of the house frame to prevent wall racking and distortion of the frame in high winds and/or the possible complete collapse of the house.

Bracing type and positions should be indicated on the plans as a dotted line on the elevations and dotted line (or some other clear indication) on the floor plan. All corners should receive bracing where possible.

Bracing is chosen to suit the individual application. In some applications, the stud is not permitted to be weakened by the cutting in of bracing so speedbrace, flat strap or structural sheet ply is used. Sheet bracing is also applied on short walls where a diagonal brace would be too steep to be effective.

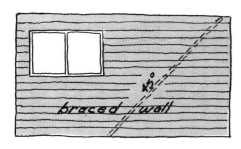

Wall Racking or Distortion
Exaggerated state of a wall without sufficient bracing. A wall that has racked only slightly out of alignment will cause wall linings and paintwork to crack.

Types of Bracing

A. Where cutting in of braces is permitted, timber braces or approved metal angle are used. End splitting of timber braces is not permitted. If necessary, nail holes should be drilled. Refer to plans and specifications for precise bracing requirements.

B. If using flat metal bracing or speed bracing, not less than two tension braces acting in opposing directions should be used in each panel. However, when fitting strap braces, ensure they are correctly tensioned. The application of speed bracing is preferred as tensioning is not required.

C. Structural plywood – This can be attached to the outside of frames in brick veneer cavities. It is the preferable method of bracing short walls instead of doglegging.

Further Bracing Types
Wall bracing can also be achieved by the use of fibre cement sheet "hardibrace" and some interior wall boards when used according to Manufacturer's specifications for that purpose.

Plywood Bracing

Plans should indicate the specific wall areas to be plywood braced: also the type and thickness of plywood.

Fixing Plywood Bracing

A. Using Flathead nails or clouts and spaced at 150mm centres around all edges and not less than 9mm in from the sheet edges and at 300mm down intermediate studs.(Nail length as specified.)

B. Using Staples, galvanized or coated and power driven: must be spaced at 100mm centres around all edges and a minimum of 9mm in from edges and at 200mm centres down intermediate studs.

If bracing panels are made up of 2 sheets, then their joins must butt together sharing a common stud.

Bracing & Squaring Frames

How to Square Frame for Bracing

Step 1 Ensure the bottom plate is straight. It can be lined up to a chalk line or a flooring join.

Step 2 Then measure the diagonals of the frame. Hold the tape on the stud marks at the same position in the opposite corner. See figure 102. Then rack the frame until both diagonals correspond. A temporary brace can be used to hold the frame square while the permanent brace is fitted.

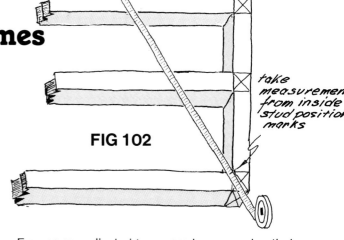

FIG 102

take measurement from inside stud position marks

Frames are adjusted to square by measuring their diagonals and holding the tape on corresponding points at each end as in figure 102.

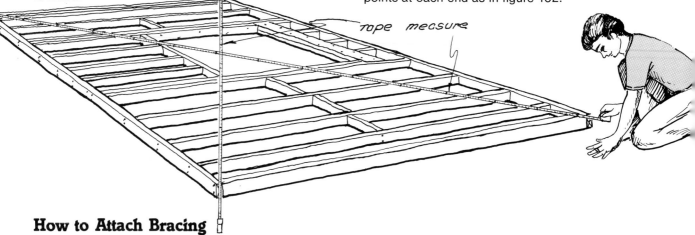

tape measure

How to Attach Bracing

Step 1 Lay the brace on its proposed position and mark a pencil line on the side of the brace at each stud crossing. Ensure the brace is held straight.

Step 2 Adjust the circular saw to slightly deeper than the depth of the brace and cut through lines marked in step 1.

Step 3 Fit brace nailing bottom end home but only partially drive in the nail at the top end. These braces may have to be adjusted when plumbing the frames after erection. *An installed angle brace will project over the face of the studs preventing linings from flush contract. Rebate for angle braces by passing the electric plane across at these points.*

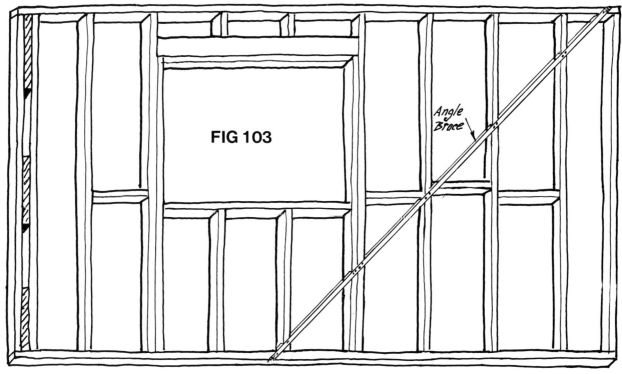

FIG 103

Angle Brace

attach cut in timber or angle brace while frames are still lying on the floor.

Wall Bracing Cont.

Speedbrace

Speed bracing or flat strap steel bracing are tension braces only and must be fitted in opposing pairs.

How to Attach

Square wall frames as on page 54 and attach the speedbraces in pairs with their ends folded under the bottom plate and over the top plate. Secure the bottom ends but only partially nail the top ends and intermediate stud crossings. Keep the braces in a straight line and at 45 degrees. Nails can be secured after the frames have been erected and plumbed.

When using speedbracing, wall linings should be nailed to the top and bottom plates with 2.8mm diameter flathead nails at 450mm centres. In some States, anchor rods are required at each end of the bracing panel and also each end of the panels anchored to the substructure with M12mm bolts. Refer to plans and specifications.

Nails
30 x 3.15 Gal. FH.

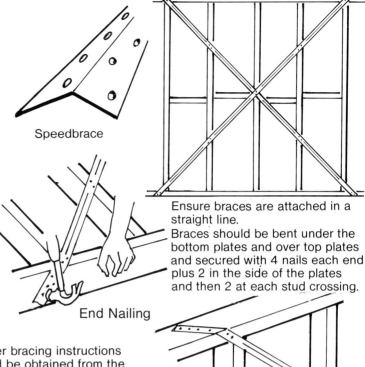

Speedbrace

End Nailing

Ensure braces are attached in a straight line.
Braces should be bent under the bottom plates and over top plates and secured with 4 nails each end plus 2 in the side of the plates and then 2 at each stud crossing.

Further bracing instructions should be obtained from the Manufacturer's instruction leaflet.

Angle Bracing

Angle braces come in 2 sizes, the smaller one is known as 'mini brace' and should only be used where studs are spaced at 450mm centres.
For installation, see page 54.
Nailing 30 x 3.15 Gal. FH. Use 2 nails on each plate and stud crossing.

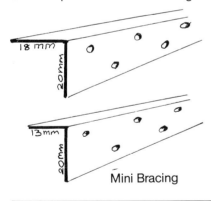

Mini Bracing

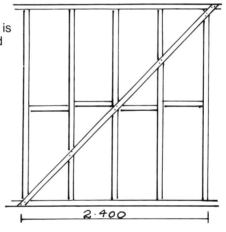

Diagonal bracing at 45 degrees

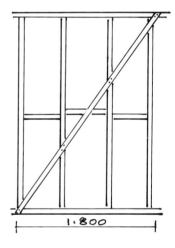

Diagonal bracing should not be steeper than the above.

Queensland Bracing Requirement

For the use of timber or approved metal angle brace.

Nailing

Approved galvanised angle brace or 75 x 15 F8 hwd timber brace. Angle brace must be fixed with 2 – 30 x 3.15 flathead gal. connector nails at each plate and stud crossing. Timber brace must be fixed with 2 – 50 x 3.75 dia. nails at each plate and stud crossing. Pre drill for end nails.

One strap, 2 framing anchors, M10 bolt or approved concrete anchor with a working load pull out strength of 3 kn. at each end of bracing panel.

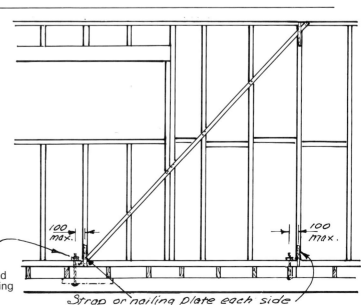

Strap or nailing plate each side of the stud wall & at both ends of the bracing panel.

Erecting Frames

Erecting Frames

To simplify straightening of bottom plates later on, spring a chalk line on the inside of the wall plate positions around the perimeter of the house prior to erecting any frames. The 4 intersecting corners of the sprung chalk line can also be measured diagonally to test for square.

Step 1 If frames are to be erected on a concrete slab, drill any anchor bolt holes through the bottom plate before erecting.

Step 2 Raise first frame into position. Tack temporary braces to walls to prevent them overturning.

Step 3 Continue to erect frames partially nailing them to the preceding frame.
Note If when raising frames into position, they have to also be lifted over protruding anchor bolts, place wooden blocks under bottom plates before erecting the frame to make it easier.

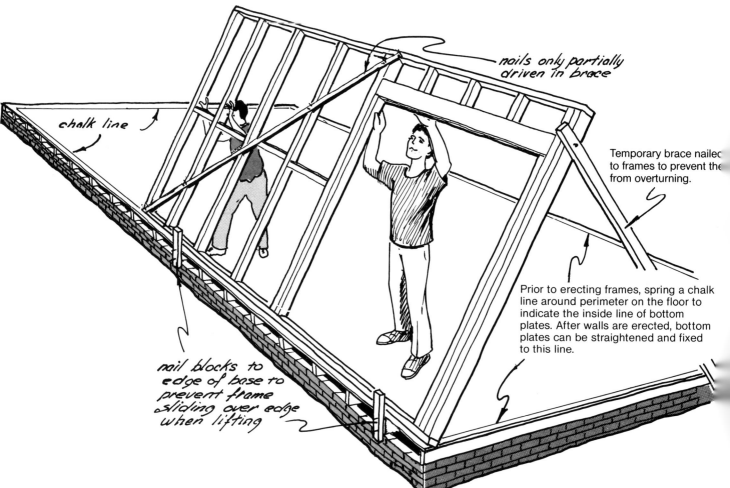

chalk line

nails only partially driven in brace

Temporary brace nailed to frames to prevent them from overturning.

Prior to erecting frames, spring a chalk line around perimeter on the floor to indicate the inside line of bottom plates. After walls are erected, bottom plates can be straightened and fixed to this line.

nail blocks to edge of base to prevent frame sliding over edge when lifting

Straightening and Fixing Bottom Plates

If the chalk line method is not adopted, then the string line and gauge block method can be applied. Attach gauge blocks of equal thickness to all external corners on the edge of the bottom plates. Then stretch a string line onto the face of these gauge blocks. Now using a spare gauge block, at regular intervals, slide it between the plate and string until it barely touches the string. Then nail the bottom plate at these points. Carry out this procedure, straightening the centres first and working towards the ends.

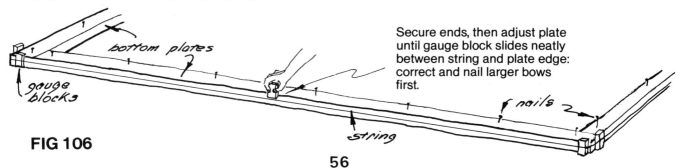

bottom plates

gauge blocks

Secure ends, then adjust plate until gauge block slides neatly between string and plate edge: correct and nail larger bows first.

nails

string

FIG 106

Plumbing the Frame

How to Plumb the Frame

Frames can be plumbed by either using a straightedge and level or by a plumb bob and gauge blocks. However, the straightedge and level method is quicker and simpler. The straightedge must be straight and parallel and must reach from the floor to the top plate. The level must be accurate. Either method should be carried out with an assistant who adjusts and secures the temporary braces.

Preparing a Straightedge

Attach small wooden blocks of equal size to each end of the straightedge. When in use, they will rest on the sides of the top and bottom plates. Their purpose is to enable the straightedge to stand free of any bows in the stud.

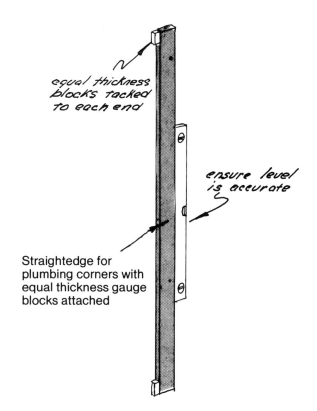

equal thickness blocks tacked to each end

ensure level is accurate

Straightedge for plumbing corners with equal thickness gauge blocks attached

level on straightedge

permanent braces

temporary brace

Step 1 Provide 100 x 50mm temporary braces to every wall, nailing top ends only to top plates. Ensure that if a brace extends above the top plate, it will not become an obstruction when constructing the roof. Have a nail driven in the bottom of the brace ready to attach the moment the level reads plumb.

Step 2 Plumb the internal and external corners using the straightedge and level. If the wall is out of plumb, release the permanent brace that was temporarily attached when constructing the frame.

Now plumb the corner again while the assistant pushes or pulls the frame into plumb position with the temporary brace. The moment it is plumb, the assistant secures the bottom end of the temporary brace.

Any top plate joins may require adjusting to permit corners to move into plumb position. After the wall is plumbed and temporarily braced, the permanent braces can be secured and nails driven home with two nails at each stud crossing. Repeat this procedure on all walls.

Straightening Top Plates

straightened top plate

brace nailed to stud below top plate

For the top plate to be straight the guage block must slide neatly between the string line and the top plate. The assistant can then secure the bottom end of the brace.

permanent bracing

temporary braces

Brace nailed to floor block or angled across to bottom plates

string

String lines are fixed tight over gauge blocks of equal thickness and taken around the perimeter of the top plates.

temporary brace

FIG 108

How to Straighten Top Plates

After all external and internal corners have been plumbed, all top plates have to be straightened.

Step 1 Drive home all nails anchoring bottom plates and tighten anchor bolts to bottom plates.

Step 2 Attach 100mm x 50mm or 75mm x 50mm temporary braces to top plate or sides of studs underneath the top plates at points where bows occur: and, or at approximately 1800mm centres. Ensure lower end of braces arrive beside the bottom of a stud on an opposite wall bottom plate or nail a 100mm x 50mm block to the floor for securing the lower ends of the braces to. Do not fix lower ends yet.

Step 3 Attach a string line to the outside perimeter of the top plate with equal thickness wooden gauge blocks at each corner under the string. Using a spare gauge block, slide it between string line and the side of the top plate while an assistant adjusts the temporary brace in or out until the gauge block slides neatly behind the string. At that moment, secure bottom end of temporary brace. Straighten all remaining top plates similiarly. See gauge block method fig 106

Step 4 All missing noggs can now be fitted. All cyclone bolts and straps can be fastened.

Hint

1. Ensure string lines are stretched tight.
2. Leave all temporary braces attached until the roof is completed.

Anchoring Wall Frames

After straightening top plates, they must be tied down. Tie down must be effective from top plate to the foundations. It is pointless tying down top plate to studs if bottom plates are not tied to studs. The bottom plate must also be tied to the base or foundations.

Any one of these methods below are commonly used. Refer to plans for specific anchorage requirements.

Anchor bolts can be extended in length by the use of female jointer couplings.

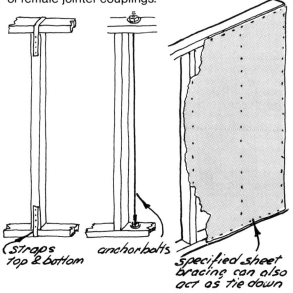

straps top & bottom   *anchorbolts*   *specified sheet bracing can also act as tie down*

Roof Construction

5

Prefabricated Roof Trusses

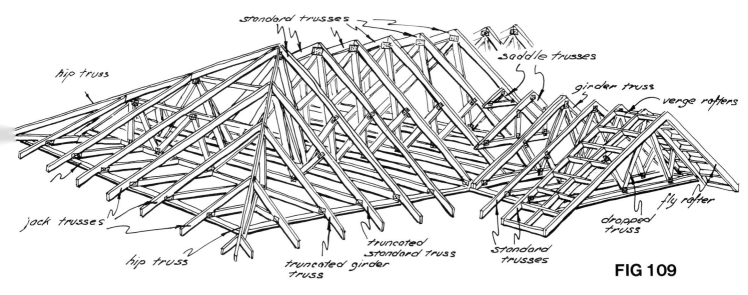

FIG 109

Roof Truss Member Identification

Prefabricated roof trusses can be used for almost all roofing designs. They are the ideal means of construction for the owner builder because of their simplicity and speed of erection. Suppliers will often come on to the site to advise on erection and many usually supply a layout plan for the positioning of trusses. Ask for this service. Roof trusses are manufactured in factory conditions on long tables using mechanical jigs. Components are joined by gang nails.

Important

Manufacturer's instructions must be carefully adhered to with regard to site handling, storage, positioning, anchorage and bracing for their guarantee to remain valid.

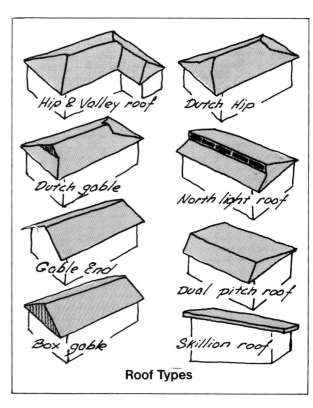

Roof Types

Truss Types

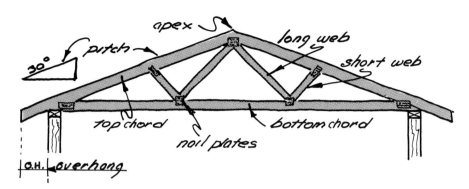

Truss Components

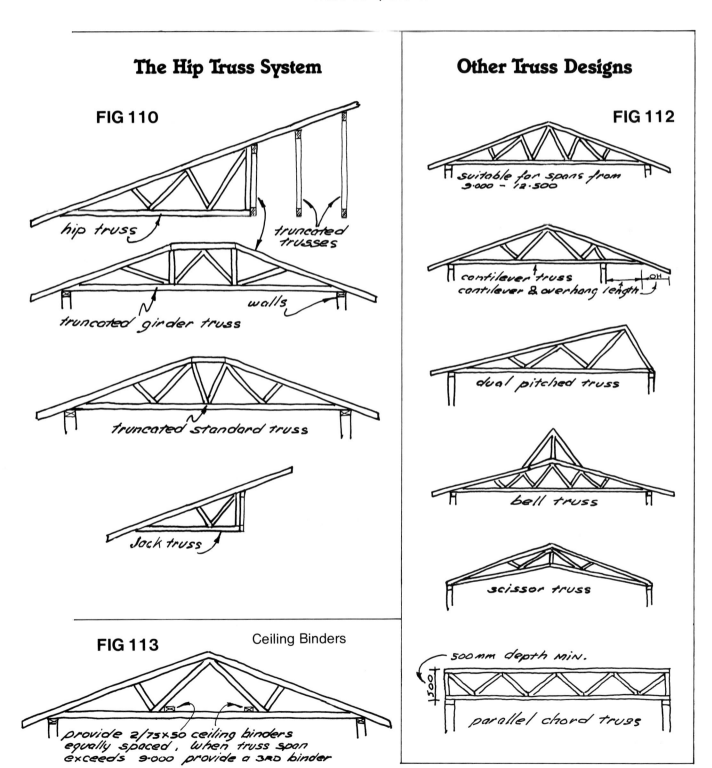

The Hip Truss System

FIG 110

hip truss

truncated trusses

truncated girder truss

walls

truncated standard truss

Jack truss

Other Truss Designs

FIG 112

suitable for spans from 9.000 – 12.500

cantilever truss
cantilever & overhang length

OH

dual pitched truss

bell truss

scissor truss

500 mm depth min.

1500

parallel chord truss

FIG 113   Ceiling Binders

provide 2/75×50 ceiling binders
equally spaced, when truss span
exceeds 9.000 provide a 3rd binder

Erecting Roof Trusses

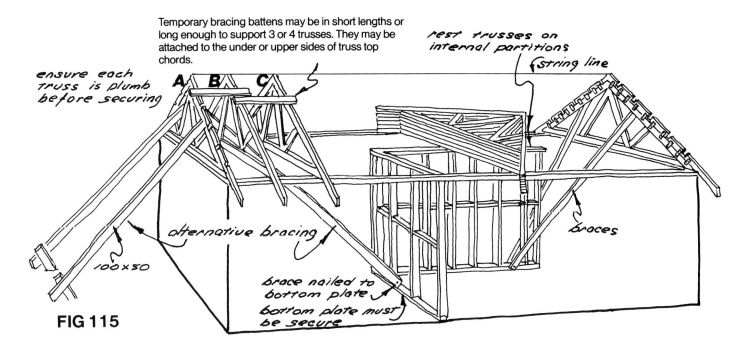

Temporary bracing battens may be in short lengths or long enough to support 3 or 4 trusses. They may be attached to the under or upper sides of truss top chords.

rest trusses on internal partitions

string line

ensure each truss is plumb before securing

A B C

alternative bracing

100 x 50

braces

brace nailed to bottom plate

bottom plate must be secure

FIG 115

How to Erect Standard Trusses on a Gable Ended Roof

Step 1 Mark off truss positions on wall plates using spacings stipulated by Manufacturer.

Step 2 Erect gable end trusses and brace according to fig.115. Plumb and tack in position. Braces can be pegged to the ground outside the building. If these braces are too long, they will prove ineffective. In this case, attach braces internally as in figure 115.

Step 3 Stretch a string line from the apex of one gable truss to the apex of the other. All intermediate trusses are positioned exactly to the string line.

Step 4 Position truss B. Temporarily brace back to truss A. Continue erecting trusses in this manner.

Step 5 After erecting all trusses, attach permanent diagonal braces.

Step 6 Fix 75mm x 50mm minimum ceiling binders to bottom cord as in figures 113 & 119

Step 7 Secure trusses to top plate with triple grips, straps or specified anchorage hardware. Do not leave truss roofs overnight without anchoring. Ensure a 12mm gap is maintained between bottom of truss and partitions to allow for roof loading. *Fix to partitions using special brackets* fig. 127A. Gable ends can finish flush with the end wall or extend past to provide eaves as in figure 128.

Step 8 Complete gable end framing pages 64 and 65.

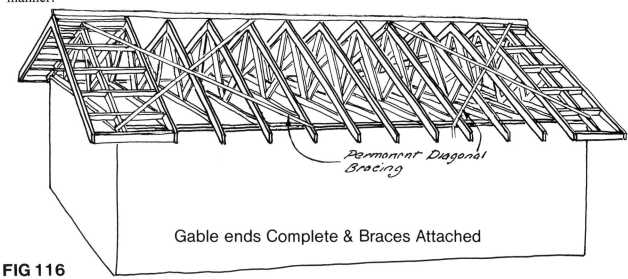

Permanent Diagonal Bracing

Gable ends Complete & Braces Attached

FIG 116

61

Diagonal Roof Bracing

Timber Bracing

Refer to plans and specifications for dimensions
and positions of diagonal timber roof bracing.
These braces are fixed to the underside of truss
top cords and at approximately 45 degrees angle
from the ridge to the wall plate; in the plane of
the roof slope; and attached to each intersection
with the top cords using 2/75mm x 3.75mm
nails. See figures 117 and 118 for attaching ends
of braces.

Note

*Specific Manufacturer's bracing requirements
must take precedence over all information and
details on this page.*

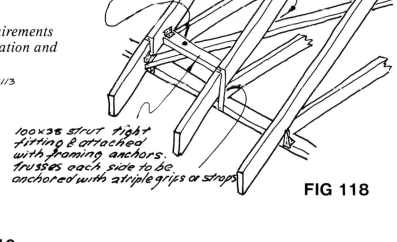

secure top end of
braces with 2/75x3.75
nails without
end splitting.

FIG 117

75x38 timber brace,
secure each intersection
with 2/75x3.75 nails.

brace bolted
to strut
with 12mm bolt

100x38 strut tight
fitting & attached
with framing anchors.
trusses each side to be
anchored with 2 triple grips or straps

FIG 118

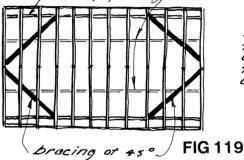

ceiling binders see fig 16 & fig 113
wall top plate.

bracing at 45°   **FIG 119**

Metal Bracing

Flat metal bracing or speed brace is effective only
in tension and therefore requires an opposing
brace. See figure 121.

Ensure braces are secured according to
Manufacturer's specifications.

FIG 120

Attaching Overlapped Joins

3 nails through
common holes
at overlapped joins.

FIG 124

4 nails

End Fixing Details

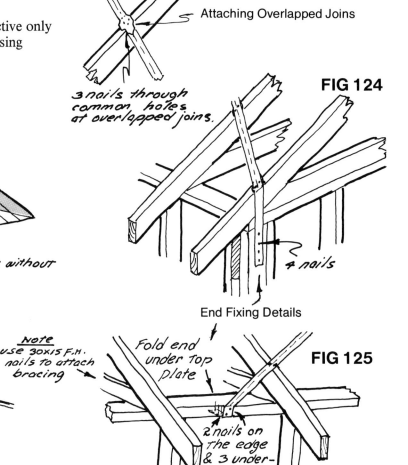

FIG 121

Battens should run continuous without
joins in shaded areas
Brace both sides of roof.

FIG 122

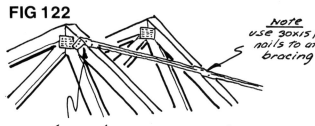

bend brace over at ends
& secure with 3 nails on
the face of the top cord.
secure the brace at every
crossing with 2 nails.

Note
use 30x15 F.H.
nails to attach
bracing

Fold end
under top
plate

FIG 125

2 nails on
the edge
& 3 under-
neath.

Roof Fixing

Manufactured roof trusses should not be secured by skew nailing. Refer to Manufacturer's specifications for recommended fixing for the particular situation. If more than one triplegrip is recommended, it is more economical in time and cost to use the strap method in figure 126B This strap has been specially designed for anchoring truss ends and nail holes are provided. The specifiction may require two straps in extreme situations or M10mm bolts are sometimes called for.

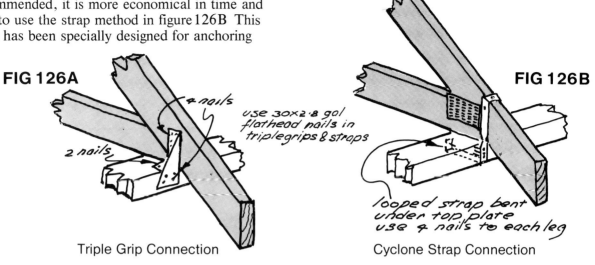

FIG 126A

4 nails

use 30x2·8 gal flathead nails in triplegrips & straps

2 nails

Triple Grip Connection

FIG 126B

looped strap bent under top plate use 4 nails to each leg

Cyclone Strap Connection

Two methods of securing partitions to truss bottom cords.

Do not secure partitions to truss bottom cords by driving nails up from the underside of top plates.

Note: For fixing truss bottom chords to bracing walls, see the required details in your state Timber Framing Manual.

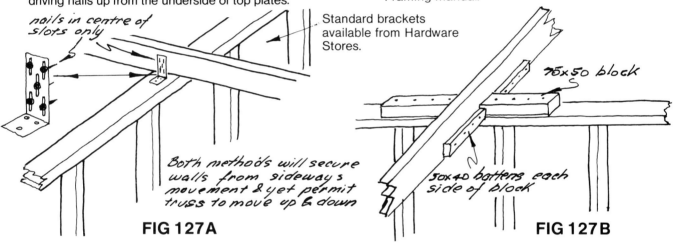

nails in centre of slots only

Standard brackets available from Hardware Stores.

Both methods will secure walls from sideways movement & yet permit truss to move up & down

FIG 127A

75x50 block

50x40 battens each side of block

FIG 127B

Gable End Finishes

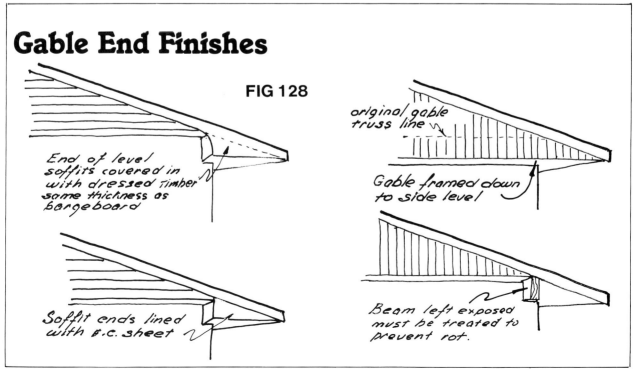

FIG 128

End of level soffits covered in with dressed Timber same thickness as bargeboard

Soffit ends lined with B.C. sheet

original gable truss line

Gable framed down to side level

Beam left exposed must be treated to prevent rot.

Gable Construction

Dropped Gable Trusses

Dropped trusses contain two top cords. The upper cord is notched on site to house the verge rafters which cantilever off the lower top cord to support the fly rafters.

How to Construct Gable End Verges

After erecting and bracing all trusses, the gable ends can be completed.

Step 1 Mark positions of all outrigger (or verge) rafters on the dropped gable truss and on the face of truss B. Notch out housings for the outriggers on dropped truss A.

Step 2 Fix outriggers in position.

Step 3 Fix last outrigger and spring a chalk line through the ends of all outriggers and trim their ends.

Step 4 Secure the fly rafter in position.

(see also HSOB page 49)

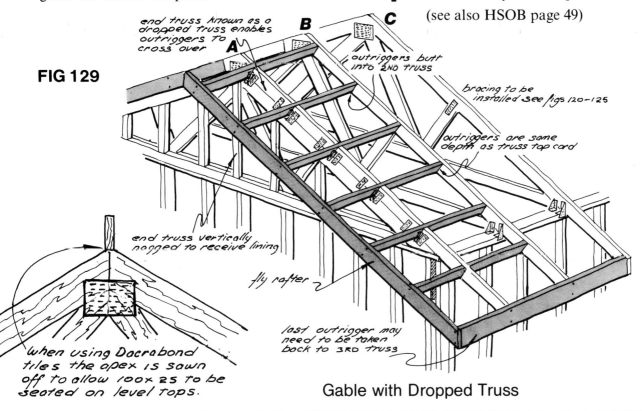

FIG 129

end truss known as a dropped truss enables outriggers to cross over

outriggers butt into 2ND truss

bracing to be installed see figs 120-125

outriggers are same depth as truss top cord

end truss vertically nogged to receive lining

fly rafter

last outrigger may need to be taken back to 3RD truss

when using Docrabond tiles the apex is sawn off to allow 100×25 to be seated on level tops.

Gable with Dropped Truss

Box Gable

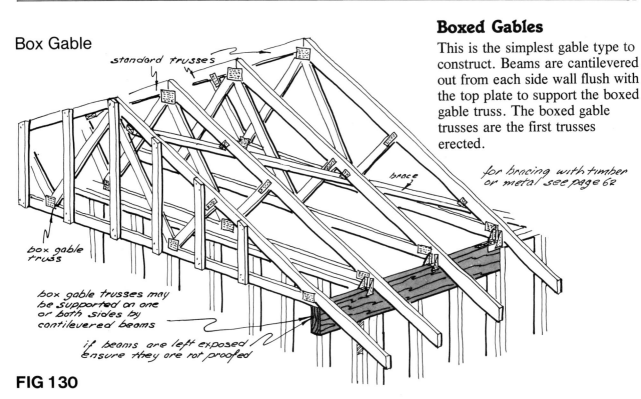

Boxed Gables

This is the simplest gable type to construct. Beams are cantilevered out from each side wall flush with the top plate to support the boxed gable truss. The boxed gable trusses are the first trusses erected.

standard trusses

brace

for bracing with timber or metal see page 62

box gable truss

box gable trusses may be supported on one or both sides by cantilevered beams

if beams are left exposed ensure they are rot proofed

FIG 130

Dutch Gables

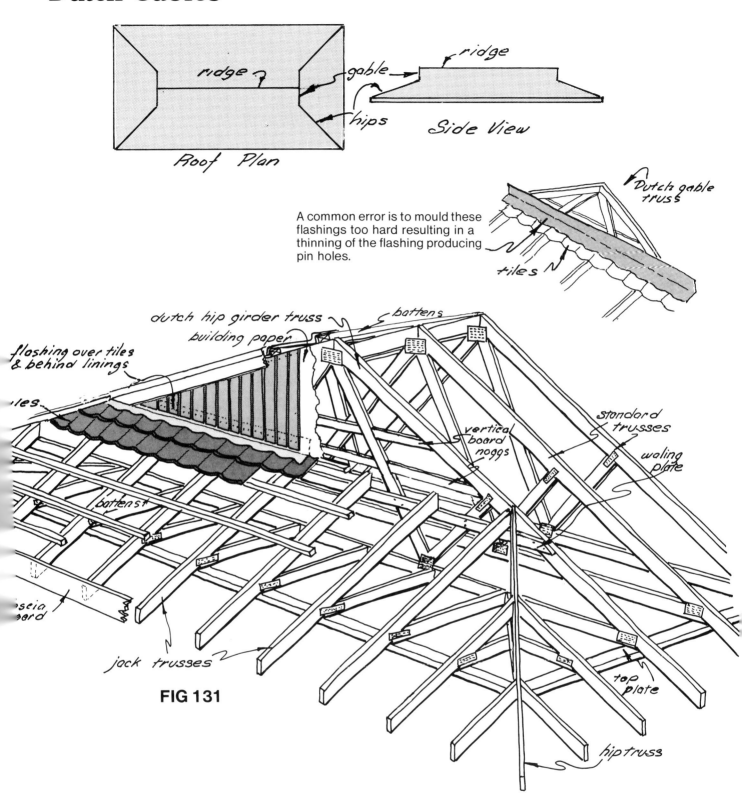

ridge

gable

ridge

hips

Roof Plan

Side View

A common error is to mould these flashings too hard resulting in a thinning of the flashing producing pin holes.

Dutch gable truss

tiles

dutch hip girder truss

building paper

battens

flashing over tiles & behind linings

tiles

Dutch gable truss

standard trusses

vertical board noggs

waling plate

battens

jack trusses

fascia board

top plate

hip truss

FIG 131

How to Erect the Dutch Gable Truss Roof

Step 1 Following the truss spacings shown on the truss plan, mark off the truss positions on the top plate. Ensure accuracy in marking the positions of the dutch hip girder trusses.

Step 2 Erect dutch hip girder truss and its counterpart at the opposite end. Then plumb and temporarily brace.

Step 3 Attach waling plate (if the Manufacturer has not already done so).

Step 4 Erect the hip trusses.

Step 5 Erect jack trusses

Step 6 Complete intermediate standard trusses as for gable roofs on page 61.

Step 7 Ensure all triple grips or anchoring straps are in place and permanent braces attached.

Hip Roofs

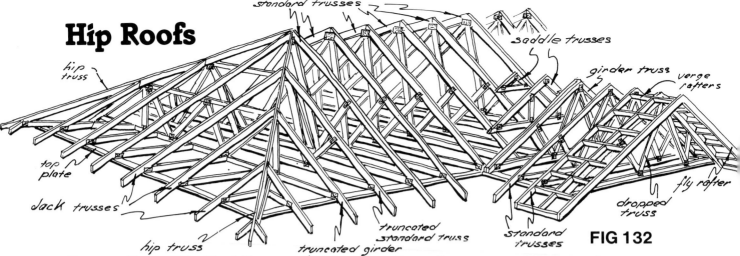

FIG 132

How to Erect Hip End Trusses

Step 1 Mark out truss positions on the wall plates at stations indicated on the Manufacturer's plan.

Step 2 Erect truncated standard truss A. Plumb and temporarily brace.

Step 3 Erect truncated girder truss B. Plumb and brace off truss A.

Step 4 Erect hip trusses C. When the hip trusses are in place, the top cord is about 25mm above the other top cords. This is intentional allowing the roof battens to butt flush up against the top cord of the hip truss.

Step 5 Finally erect remaining jack trusses E.

Step 6 Secure all truss ends permanently using specified fixings.

Step 7 After completing the first hip end, operations are then transferred to the opposite end of the roof to erect any other hip ends or gable trusses. A string line is then attached between the two ends at the apex and all intermediate standard trusses D are then erected to the string line. See figure 134. Bracing and truss ends should then be fixed according to Manufacturer's requirements.

Note

A stud should be positioned directly underneath the truncated girder truss at each end.

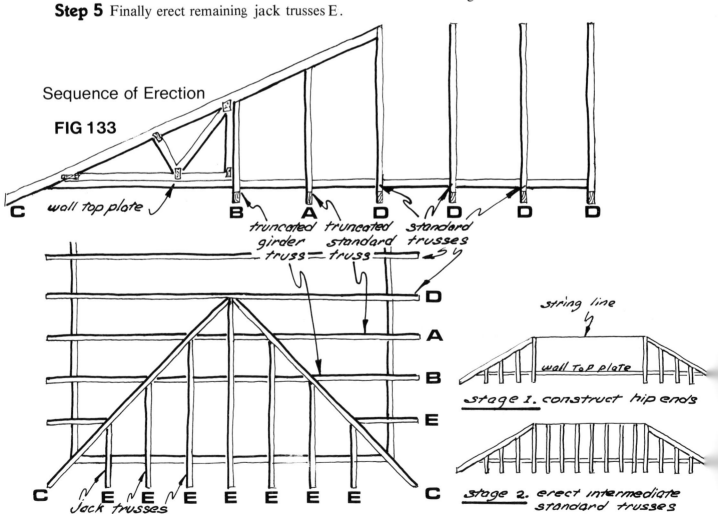

Sequence of Erection

FIG 133

Sequence of erection should begin with "A" through to "E" in alphabetical order.

FIG 134

Roofs with Valleys

Sequence of Erection

Sequence of erection should begin with "A"
through to "G" in alphabetical order.

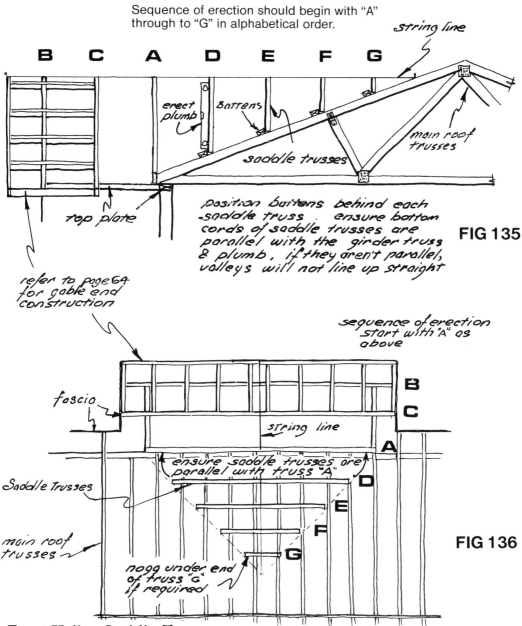

FIG 135

FIG 136

How to Erect Valley Saddle Trusses

Valley saddle trusses are erected after the
installation of the standard trusses to the main
roof has been completed.

Step 1 Erect truss A. Plumb and temporarily
brace.

Step 2 Erect gable truss B. Plumb and
temporarily brace as for a normal gable end as in
figure 115 page 61

Step 3 Attach a string line on the apex of truss
B through to the main roof as in figure 135.
Ensure it is level, square and parallel with the
main building. It should also line up with the apex
of truss A. Attach the string to a temporary nogg
fitted between the trusses on the main roof.

Step 4 Position remaining trusses fixing battens
on the lower side of the saddle trusses for extra
support. See figure 135.

Step 5 Secure trusses to wall top plate as on
page 63 and attach diagonal wind braces as on
page 62.

Step 6 Complete gable framing.

Note A

A girder truss at Truss A is used when there is no
supporting wall below.

Note B

If the smallest saddle truss is not long enough to
span the main trusses, install supporting noggs
below the unsupported ends.

Sloping Ceilings

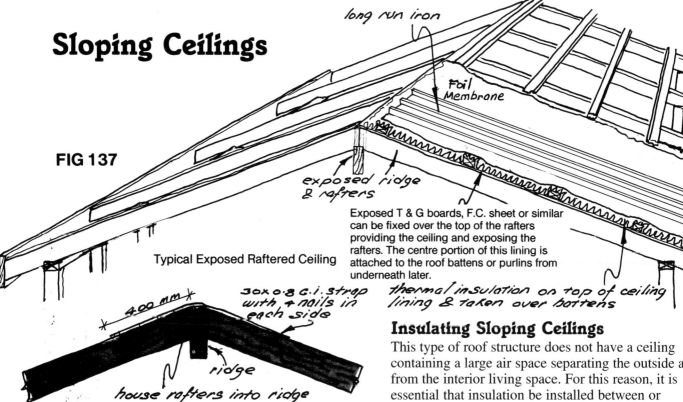

FIG 137

Typical Exposed Raftered Ceiling

long run iron

Foil Membrane

exposed ridge & rafters

Exposed T & G boards, F.C. sheet or similar can be fixed over the top of the rafters providing the ceiling and exposing the rafters. The centre portion of this lining is attached to the roof battens or purlins from underneath later.

thermal insulation on top of ceiling lining & taken over battens

400 mm

30 x 0.8 G.i. strap with 4 nails in each side

ridge

house rafters into ridge

FIG 138

Rafter to Ridge Beam Connection

How to Erect Exposed Rafters

Step 1 Mark position of rafters as indicated on the house plan. Then cut rafters to length. It is advisable to cut and test one pair in position before cutting the remaining rafters.

Step 2 Erect the ridge board by fitting it in position between two pairs of rafters at opposite ends. Alternatively, if it is supported by walls at each end, then cut and fit into position. *(Stations of rafters should be transferred on to the ridgeboard prior to raising into position).*

Step 3 Remaining rafters are now attached to the ridgeboard and top wall plate.

Step 4 Ceiling lining is laid on top of rafters and secured, straps are attached over the apex of rafters as in fig 138.

Step 5 Fix roofing battens according to spacings indicated on plan.

Step 6 Lay insulation across the battens. Ensure insulation blankets fit tightly together. Attach roof cladding according to plans or Manufacturer's specifications.

Insulating Sloping Ceilings

This type of roof structure does not have a ceiling containing a large air space separating the outside air from the interior living space. For this reason, it is essential that insulation be installed between or above the rafters. As most sloping ceilings have exposed rafters, the insulation must be laid over and between the battens or purlins as in fig 137. Attach reflective foil membrane over insulation and beneath roof cladding and seal joins.

Note: Wool fibre insulation taken over the battens can cause problems when driving roofing screws as the wool fibres wind around the screws causing bulging of the cladding in the fixing points. Lay wool batts between battens or purlins.

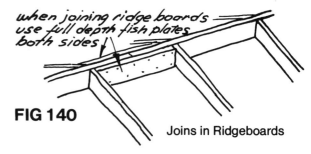

when joining ridge boards use full depth fish plates both sides

FIG 140

Joins in Ridgeboards

Recommendations for Exposed Raftered Roofs

Rafters without ceiling joist or collar tie restraint, and which are only supported or tied together at the ridge, exert increased outward pressure known as 'rafter spread'. For this reason it is generally preferable not to apply this system to the whole house roof but rather restrict it to a portion or portions only.

For simplicity of construction, Fig 139 is preferred to Fig 138.

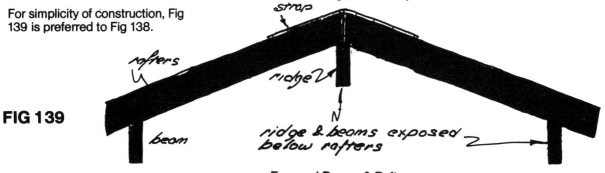

strap

rafters

ridge

FIG 139

beam

ridge & beams exposed below rafters

Exposed Beams & Rafters

Near Flat Roofs

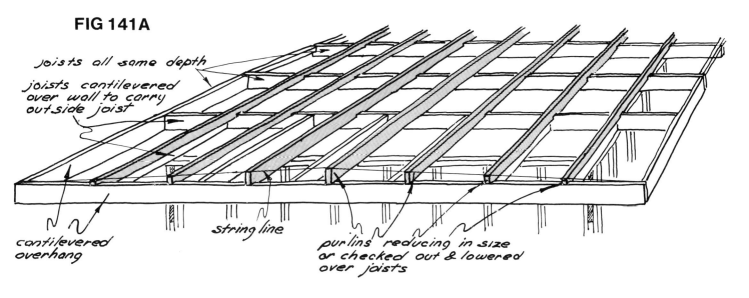

FIG 141A

joists all same depth

joists cantilevered over wall to carry outside joist

cantilevered overhang

string line

purlins reducing in size or checked out & lowered over joists

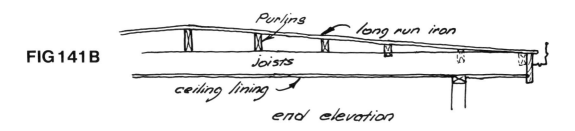

FIG 141B

Purlins

long run iron

Joists

ceiling lining

end elevation

Purlins Reducing in Height

Constructing Near Flat Roofs

Roof purlins can act as ceiling joists. Alternative methods of construction are possible. The one illustrated in figures 141A and B has joists cantilevered over wall plates to create eaves and uses the same depth joist throughout. The purlins reduce in height thus providing the fall in pitch and eliminate the need for battens.

Figure 142 also eliminates the need for battens and all purlins are of the same depth attached to the sloping or raked wall previously constructed to the correct pitch.

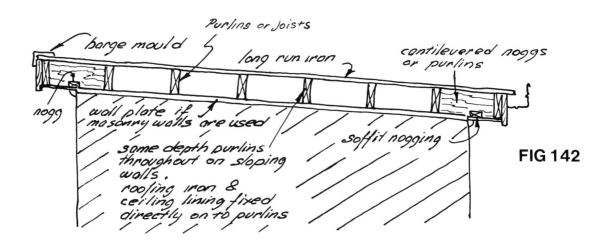

Purlins or Joists

barge mould

long run iron

cantilevered noggs or purlins

nogg

wall plate if masonry walls are used

some depth purlins throughout on sloping walls.
roofing iron & ceiling lining fixed directly on to purlins

soffit nogging

FIG 142

Wall Tops Raked to Roof Pitch

6

Finishing

Weatherboard Sidings

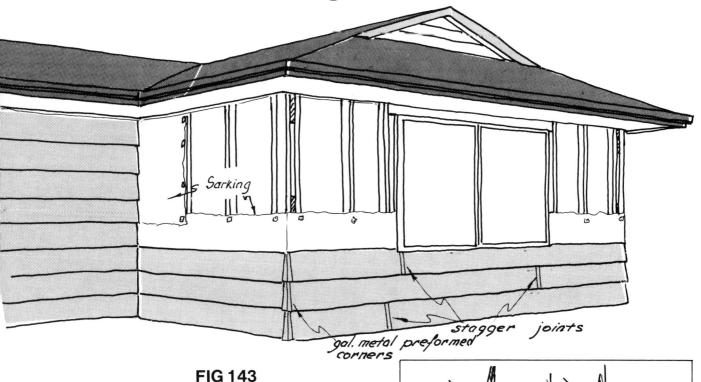

FIG 143

Weatherboards come in a variety of shapes and materials. These fixing instructions will apply to timber weatherboards, fibre cement and compressed wood. However, with the latter two, further instruction pamphlets are available from the Manufacturers. When ordering weatherboards, remember that the installed width is less than the overall width because of the lap required. See figures 145 and 146.

Windows and doors are installed first, then head and side flashings attached. The weatherboard ends are cut to butt snugly into the frames to provide a further weather barrier. On timber joinery, after fitting the weatherboards, a dressed timber facing of hardwood or treated pine approximately 68mm x 19mm is nailed over the door or window frame edge. This overlaps the ends of the weatherboards and provides the necessary weather protection.

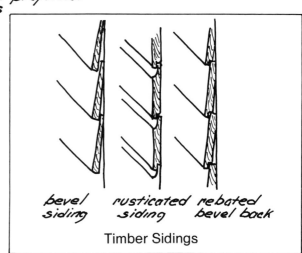

Timber Sidings

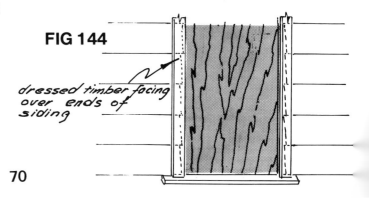

FIG 144

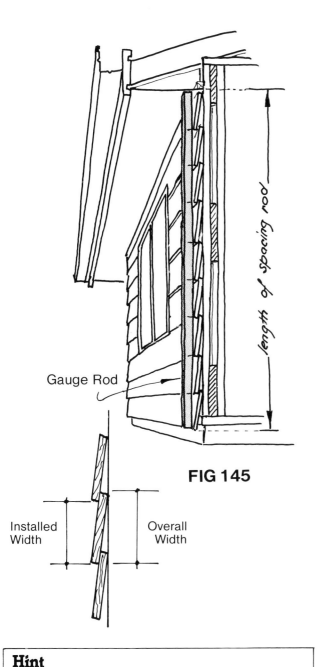

Gauge Rod

FIG 145

Installed Width   Overall Width

Hint

If working alone, boards can be supported on nails partially driven either end of the chalk line. Nail holes are filled later by the painter.

How to Fix Weatherboards

Step 1 Measure the height of the wall to be cladded. Take a spacing rod (50mm x 20mm or similar) and transfer the wall height on to the rod. Then divide the rod by the width of the weatherboards being used minus their overlaps. See figure 145.

Step 2 Fix the packing strip to support the lowest board. See figure 146. This packing strip can be attached to the walls or the weatherboard. Spring a chalk line through the proposed top edge of the first weatherboard. Ensure it is level and attach the first board to the line. If using timber or compressed wood weatherboards, ensure all end grains receive a coat of wood primer. This first board should lap any base wall or slab edges as in figure 146.

Step 3 Find the line of the second board by holding the bottom of the spacing rod flush with the bottom of the first board. Transfer the position of the second board from the spacing rod and likewise at the opposite end of the wall. Spring a chalk line to these marks. Secure the second board to the chalk line. Repeat this procedure for all remaining boards. See figure 146.

Nailing

Drive nails above the tongue or top edge of preceding boards. Punch nails below the surface unless fibre cement boards are being used. In this case, nails should be driven through the preceding boards and left flush with the surface see manufacturer's instructions. Take care the hammer head is not leaving an impression.

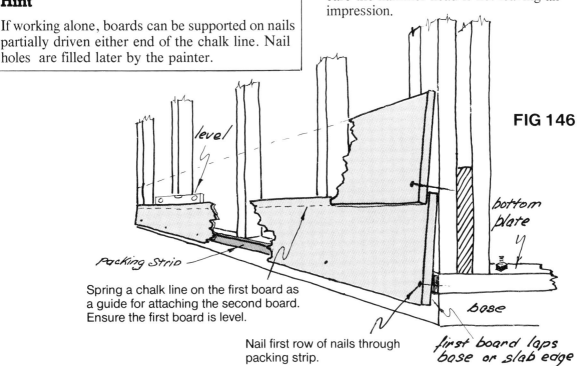

FIG 146

level

bottom plate

packing strip

base

Spring a chalk line on the first board as a guide for attaching the second board. Ensure the first board is level.

Nail first row of nails through packing strip.

first board laps base or slab edge

Attaching the First Boards

Weatherboard Sidings Cont.

How to Scribe Boards to Fit Internal Corner Boards

Method 1 Gauge Block Method Figure 147A&B
Position the board to be scribed up against the fixed board and at the same height. This board can be supported on nails. Take a dressed piece of 50mm x 20mm or similar 100mm long. Cut one end on a bevel at the approximate angle at which the boards slope. Gauge a pencil line on to the loose board by sliding the gauge block down the fixed board. The bevelled end should be butted against the loose board and the pencil following tightly against the gauge block. See figure 147B Instead of a gauge block, many tradesmen use a carpenter's rule.

Method 2 Using Wing Dividers
Position the board to be scribed as in Method 1. Using a pair of wing dividers, guide one arm of the dividers to follow the fixed board while allowing the other arm to scribe a parallel line on to the loose board.

External Corners

External corners are usually mitred. Just prime the end grain and nail the mitre tightly together. With manmade boards, Aluminium soakers are applied over the corner.

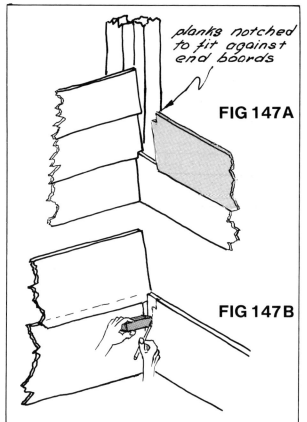

FIG 147A

FIG 147B

Sliding a block of dressed wood in one hand and with a pencil in the other, scribe the bevel line onto the loose board.

Scribing internal Corner Boards

Vertical Board Sidings

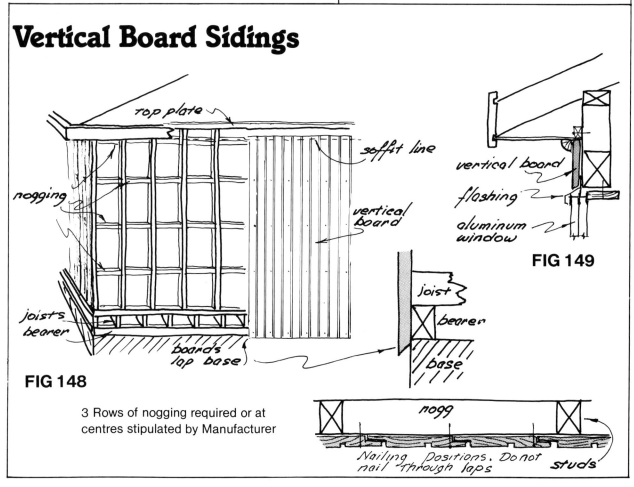

FIG 148

3 Rows of nogging required or at centres stipulated by Manufacturer

FIG 149

72

Installing Aluminium Windows

Aluminium windows are simple to install if reveals are prefitted, which is normally the case, it is a good idea to have a number of wedges cut beforehand. These should be about 100-125mm long and taper from 6mm to nothing or use strips of D.P.C. or hardboard. These will be used to pack the frame plumb and level.

Installing Aluminium Windows with Prefitted Reveals

Prior to installing, plane off half a millimetre from the back edge of the reveals to enable architraves to rest tight against the reveals. Be careful not to remove any wood from the inner edge, see fig 153.

Step 1 Place the window in the opening from the outside. Drive a temporary nail 75-100mm long into the timber head at an angle down and over the top of the window to prevent it from falling out.

Step 2 From the inside, pack up the sill reveal until level and straight using the wedges or packing. Now ensure the reveal sill is flush with internal linings. If linings have not been installed, hold a piece of the proposed linings on the face of the wall framing beside the sill and adjust the sill in or out until it rests flush with the lining, see fig 152. The sill can now be nailed but leave nails protruding until sides have been straightened and plumbed.

Step 3 Repeat the above procedure for the side reveals, plumbing and wedging. Then adjust the frame until the reveals rest flush with the proposed wall linings. Avoid using nails, wedges or packing above the head reveal. A clear space of 12mm should be maintained for shrinkage. If a sharp bow is encountered in the head reveal, this is straightened with the architrave later. When complete, the sliding or hopper sash should, when closed, be parallel with the frame.
This method of installation is also applicable for the installation of timber window joinery.

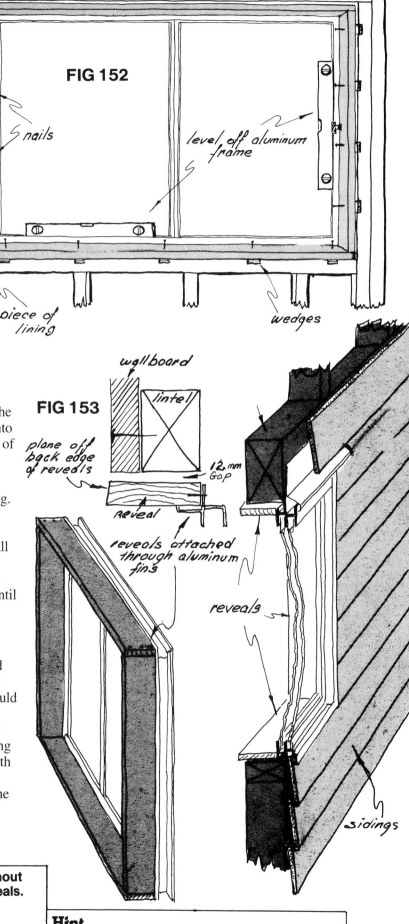

FIG 152

FIG 153

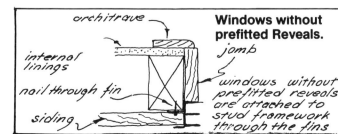

Windows without prefitted Reveals.

Hint

When testing the frame for level or plumb, rest the level on the aluminium frame, not the timber reveals.

Installing Aluminium Sliding Doors

Steps 1, 2 & 3

Step 4

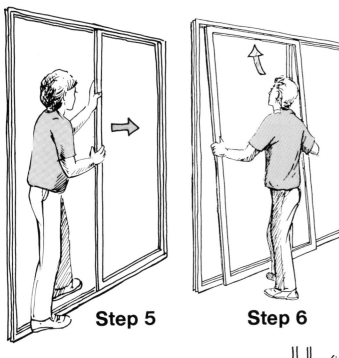

Step 5   **Step 6**

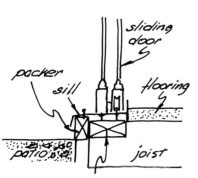

Noggs or full length timber under sill.

On Timber Floors

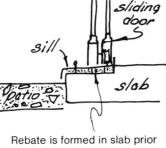

Rebate is formed in slab prior to pouring concrete. Aluminium sill can be bedded level and straight in compo (sand and cement 3 to 1

On Concrete Floors

Installing Aluminium Sliding Doors

When resting on timber floors, the aluminium sill should be fully supported on a level timber base. On concrete floors, the sill can be bedded in compo (sand & cement 3 to 1) and packed until level and straight or simply screwed to the concrete floor using masonry plugs and the sill-floor joint silicone sealed.

Step 1 Sit frame in opening already prepared.

Step 2 Before bedding or screwing down sill, check jambs for plumb as the sill may require sliding sideways.

Step 3 Make sure head, jamb and sill flashings are in place. Secure sill in position.

Step 4 Wedge jambs until they are plumb and straight, fixing top screws first.
Screw fix in grooves suggested by the Manufacturer or holes provided. Some Manufacturers will supply aluminium frames with timber reveals already fitted to frames. In this case, nail through reveals to plumb and straighten. Screws will still be required in the aluminium frame later.

Step 5 Insert fixed panel by raising up in to head track first and then lowering. Then push tightly into side frame. Screw fix through the frame into the fixed panel frame and fix head L bracket if one is provided for securing fixed panel.

Step 6 Install door in the same manner. Adjust the wheels until the door, when almost closed, shows a parallel gap between door and frame. Fit handle and lock by following the Manufacturer's instructions.

Garage Doors

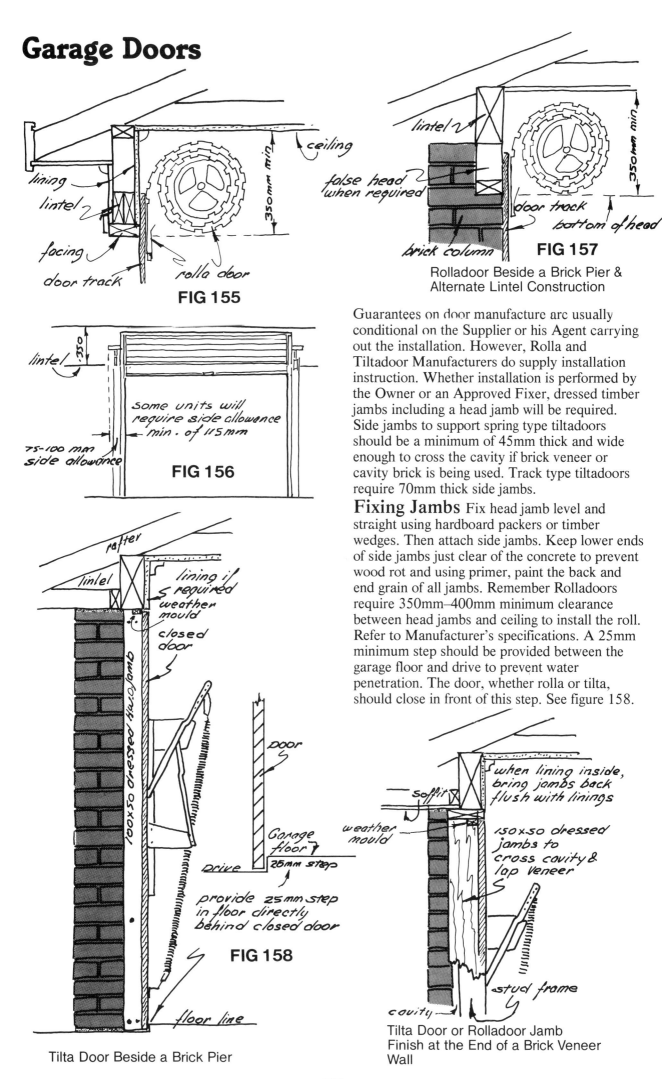

FIG 155

FIG 157

Rolladoor Beside a Brick Pier &
Alternate Lintel Construction

FIG 156

Guarantees on door manufacture are usually conditional on the Supplier or his Agent carrying out the installation. However, Rolla and Tiltadoor Manufacturers do supply installation instruction. Whether installation is performed by the Owner or an Approved Fixer, dressed timber jambs including a head jamb will be required. Side jambs to support spring type tiltadoors should be a minimum of 45mm thick and wide enough to cross the cavity if brick veneer or cavity brick is being used. Track type tiltadoors require 70mm thick side jambs.

Fixing Jambs
Fix head jamb level and straight using hardboard packers or timber wedges. Then attach side jambs. Keep lower ends of side jambs just clear of the concrete to prevent wood rot and using primer, paint the back and end grain of all jambs. Remember Rolladoors require 350mm–400mm minimum clearance between head jambs and ceiling to install the roll. Refer to Manufacturer's specifications. A 25mm minimum step should be provided between the garage floor and drive to prevent water penetration. The door, whether rolla or tilta, should close in front of this step. See figure 158.

FIG 158

Tilta Door Beside a Brick Pier

Tilta Door or Rolladoor Jamb
Finish at the End of a Brick Veneer
Wall

75

Stair Construction

Staircases

Stairs and their proportions determine the stairwell dimensions. A minimum of 2 metres head height is required above steps measured vertically above nosings. See figure 159. Risers and treads must be constant throughout. This includes the first and last risers. A variation in risers and tread dimensions can cause accidents.

Timber Sizes

Stringers: from 200mm-300mm deep and 40mm-50mm thick depending on span.
Risers: 19mm thick minimum.
Treads: 35mm-50mm thick depending on tread length.

How to Construct a Staircase

Step 1   Establish tread and riser dimensions by dividing the floor to floor height (Total rise) into a suitable number of risers each rise being approximately 175mm. Then calculate the tread depth in proportion to the rise according to "Ideal Stair Proportions". Adjust both measurements to conform to the total rise and total going. Treads are usually between 250mm and 300mm deep and risers between 150mm and 190mm in height. Risers should not exceed 190mm high and treads should not be less than 250mm deep.
The triangle created by the total run and rise with its ensuing intersecting angle can be drawn on the floor and all measurements established there.

Step 2   Riser and tread faces are indicated on the stringer using the rafter square and working from the 'setting out line'. The 'setting out line' is gauged the length of the stringer along the point of intersection where the riser line meets the top of tread line. This line is best found by first gauging the line of nosings in pencil the length of the stringer 40mm below the stringer top. The riser height and tread depth is established and marked on the rafter square. The square is now held on the stringer with riser tread positions over the nosing line. The nosing depth is now deducted measuring square off the intersection where the square meets the nosing line as in figure 160A. A pencil gauge or combination square is set to this new point and a line drawn the length of the stringer. This becomes the 'setting out line'. See figure 160B. (Nosings are usually the depth of one tread thickness.)
The fence is now attached to the square as in figure 161. The riser height and tread depth marks on the square must now intersect the new setting out line.
The fence enables tread and riser lines to be repeated accurately.

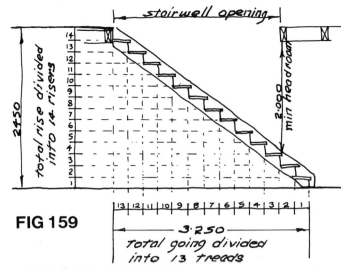

FIG 159

Total Going = 3250 ÷ 13 tread's = 250mm tread's
Total Rise = 2450 ÷ 14 risers = 175mm risers

Ideal Stair Proportions

The following calculation can be carried out to find the correct proportions. The sum of one riser plus one tread should equal between 430mm-460mm.
An alternative calculation is "The tread plus twice the riser should equal between 585mm-650mm".

To find 'setting out line' firstly guage the line of nosings 40mm below the stringer top. Then holding the square on the line at 'rise' and 'going' positions. Mark the 'setting out line' point measuring square off the tongue of the square and to the depth of the nosing from the nosing line.

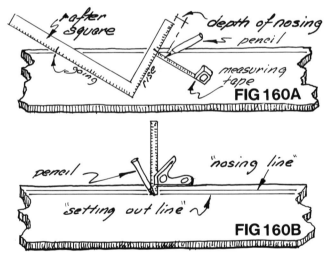

FIG 160A

FIG 160B

Set the combination square to the depth of this new point and guage the 'setting out line' the length of the stringer.

A slotted fence is fitted to the square with riser and tread positions over the 'setting out line'. Treads and riser lines are now marked out.

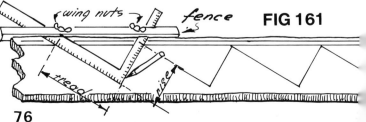

FIG 161

76

Step 3. The faces of treads and risers are now marked by sliding the square along the stringer. Accuracy in the placement of the square on each previously marked riser and tread intersection is important and a sharp pencil is essential. The marked out stringer can be checked by laying the stringer on the triangle previously marked on the floor.

Undersides of treads and risers are marked out using templates of ply or masonite.

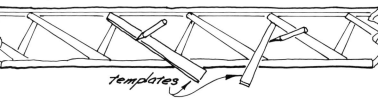

FIG 162A

Step 4 After marking the tops and faces of treads and risers, mark their back edges allowing for the tapering wedge to be inserted.
This is carried out by using tread and riser templates as a guide. See figure 162A. The templates are cut out of ply or masonite and must include the thickness of the tread or riser whichever is being cut plus the thickness and shape of the tapering wedge. It is best to cut the wedges prior to making these templates to guarantee the correct taper is allowed for. All wedges must be of identical shape. They are best cut on a table saw using a jig. Local joinery shops will usually cut them inexpensively.
When marking the shape of the tread template, include the nosing. The tread template is laid up to the nosing line along the previously marked tread line. The riser template is laid on the previously marked riser line.
Repeat these 4 steps on the other stringer.

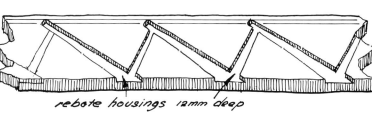

rebate housings 12mm deep

FIG 162B

Step 5 Housings can now be cut out using either the saw and chisel or electric router. Cut housings to a depth of 12mm. **162B**

Step 6 Cut treads and risers to length and attach 42mm x 19mm riser supports to underside of treads. See figure 163A

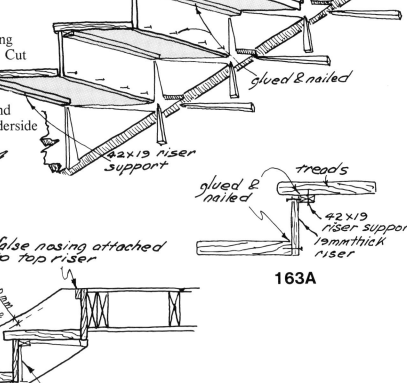

glued & nailed

42×19 riser support

glued & nailed

treads

42×19 riser support 19mm thick riser

163A

handrail

865mm min

false nosing attached to top riser

40mm

nosing line

plumb cut bottom end of stringers 40mm in front of nosings

40 mm

wedges

stringer

square off heel of stringer to rest on floor

Step 7 Now assemble stairs by first installing the top and bottom treads, then the remaining treads. Risers can now be fitted, wedging, glueing and nailing them into position. Stairs containing closed risers as illustrated, can be constructed without wedges. However without them, squeaking and creaking stairs are inevitable. These basic instructions on marking out stringers applies to all staircases whether they contain closed risers or not.

support bottom end of stringer on joist or solid nogging

77

Stair Construction Cont.

How to Prepare Formwork for Concrete Stairs

Step 1 Commence by laying bearers, toms and decking.

Step 2 Then erect stringer and riser formwork.

Step 3 Attach riser and joist cleats.

Step 4 Insert reinforcing mesh from the top and position into concrete according to plans and specification.

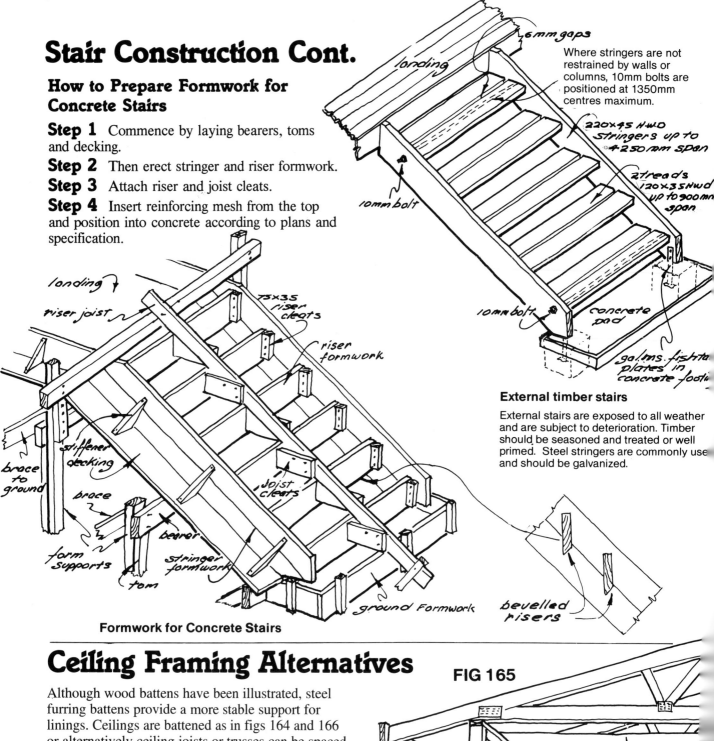

Where stringers are not restrained by walls or columns, 10mm bolts are positioned at 1350mm centres maximum.

Formwork for Concrete Stairs

External timber stairs

External stairs are exposed to all weather and are subject to deterioration. Timber should be seasoned and treated or well primed. Steel stringers are commonly used and should be galvanized.

Ceiling Framing Alternatives

Although wood battens have been illustrated, steel furring battens provide a more stable support for linings. Ceilings are battened as in figs 164 and 166 or alternatively ceiling joists or trusses can be spaced at 600mm centres and apply 12.5mm Gyprock directly to the underside of the truss bottom chords. (Overall costs are not increased). Where trusses are spaced over 600mm centres, a ceiling joist may be located between each truss as in fig 165.

Whichever method is used, support will be required around the cornice line for attaching the cornice or scocia. This can be in the form of an extra joist, batten or row of noggs.

A simple and quick method of battening can be seen

FIG 165

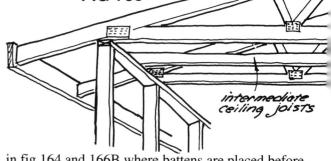

in fig 164 and 166B where battens are placed before erecting roof trusses. This method is also excellent where the batten is being used to increase the thickness of the wall top plates. Wider battens are used along the top plates to enable their edges to support the ceiling lining.

Ceiling Battening
Ceiling battening also used to increase the thickness of wall top plates.

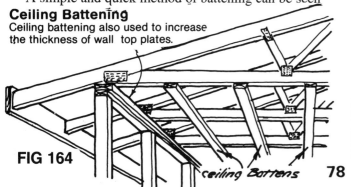

FIG 164

Manhole

Find a suitable position for the manhole and nogg to a trim size of 600mm x 500mm minimum.

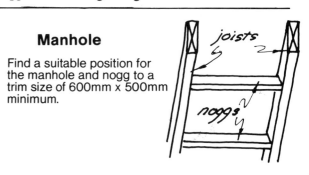

Ceiling Joists & Battens Cont.

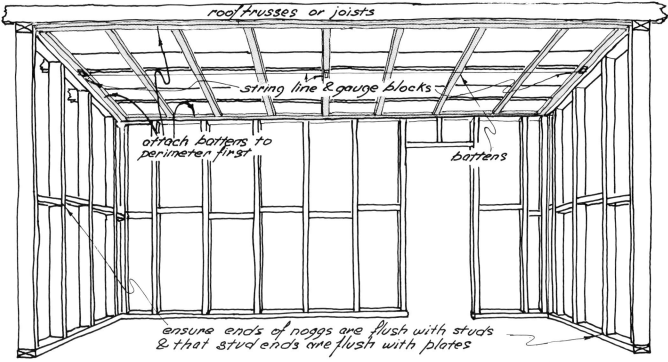

roof trusses or joists

string line & gauge blocks

attach battens to perimeter first

battens

ensure ends of noggs are flush with studs & that stud ends are flush with plates

FIG 166A

How to Erect Ceiling Battens

Step 1 Establish the lowest joist or truss bottom chord add the thickness of the batten and transfer this height around the wall perimeter using a chalk line

Step 2 Mark on the perimeter walls all the proposed batten positions.

Step 3 Fix both opposite side wall battens. Pack down to the chalk line using hardboard or wedges.

Step 4 Attach intermediate battens. Pack down ends to the chalk line. To straighten the centres of intermediate battens, a string line is stretched across the battens and attached to the two opposite side wall battens previously fitted. The gauge block method of straightening is applied as in figure166A.Battens are packed down to the string line and secured.

Alternative quick battening method: Battens are attached over top plates prior to installing roof trusses. After trusses are installed, the sagging battens are nailed up to the truss bottom chords from underneath. **FIG 166B**

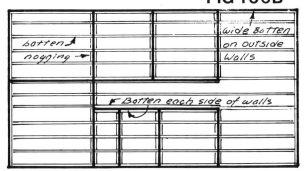

batten

nogging

wide batten on outside walls

Batten each side of walls

Solid black lines represent top plates of walls. Battens are placed each side of partitions. On load bearing walls, wide battens can be laid over the top plates with sufficient edge lap to support ceiling sheets.

Straightening Studs

Prior to fixing any external or internal wall linings, any badly bowed studs should be straightened. Wedges are cut approximately 100mm long with a taper from 6mm to nothing. A saw cut is made on the hollow side of the stud to half the depth of the stud maximum at the centre of the bow. Wedges are driven in until the stud is forced straight. The weakened stud is then strengthened by nailing 50mm x 25mm x 600mm long cleats to either side of the saw cut using 4 x 50mm nails on each side.

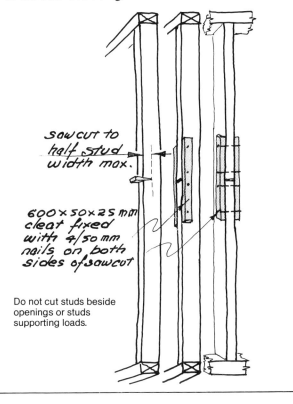

saw cut to half stud width max.

600 x 50 x 25 mm cleat fixed with 4/50 mm nails on both sides of sawcut

Do not cut studs beside openings or studs supporting loads.

Door Installation

How to Hang Doors

Step 1 Check opening width and height. For example, a 820mm door and using 19mm thick jambs, the trim openings should be:

Door	820mm
Jamb 19mm each side	38
Allowance for plumbing jambs	10
Clearance between door & jamb 2mm each side	4
Total trim width should be	872mm
Total height should be:	
Door	2040mm
Head	19
Allowance for floor coverings depending on carpet & underlay	20
For vinyl flooring allow 12mm.	
Clearance between head jamb and door	3
Total trim height	2082mm

Step 2 Square lines across studs to indicate the top of jambs. See figure 167A. This height will equal the door height plus the 3mm gap between door top and head jamb, plus floor covering allowance of 20mm for carpet or 12mm for vinyl. After marking these heights, packers of dampcourse or hardboard can be tacked to the hinge side stud where necessary to provide a plumb surface for attaching the jamb. A straightedge and level are used for plumbing the packers, see figure 167B.

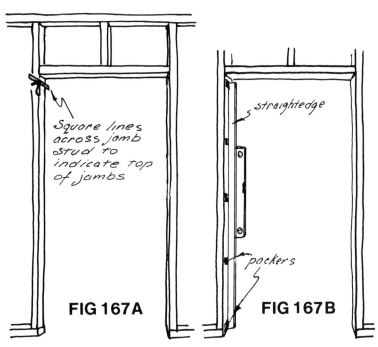

FIG 167A   FIG 167B

Square lines across jamb stud to indicate top of jambs

straightedge

packers

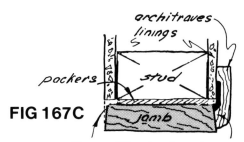

FIG 167C

Plane off back edge of jambs to enable architraves to fit tightly

Step 3 Hinge side jamb is now cut to the length previously marked on the jamb stud. Now, with a plane, remove the back edges from both edges of the jamb as in figure 167C. The hinge positions can now be marked on the jamb 200mm up from the bottom and 200mm down from the top.

Step 4 Wedge the door into a door block as in figure 167D and carefully remove the back edges from both edges of the door as in figure 167E. Hold the hinge jamb on the hinge edge of the door and transfer the hinge positions across on to the door accurately, allowing for the head jamb plus the 3mm gap between door and head jamb. The hinges can now be attached to the door. (Use hinges that do not require housings.)

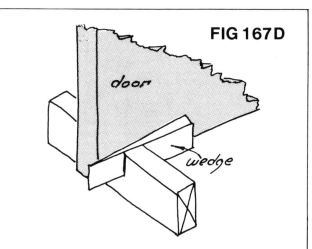

FIG 167D

door

wedge

Make a door block from 100mm x 50mm stock approximately 450mm long. Cut a slot in the chock 50mm-75mm deep and slightly larger than the thickness of the door. One side of the slot has a square cut: the opposite side 6mm out of square to allow for a wedge to slide in.

Step 5 Attach the hinge jamb onto the previously prepared jamb studs with 65mm nails ensuring a flush fit with linings or slightly proud. For thicker jambs, use longer nails.

Door Installation Cont.

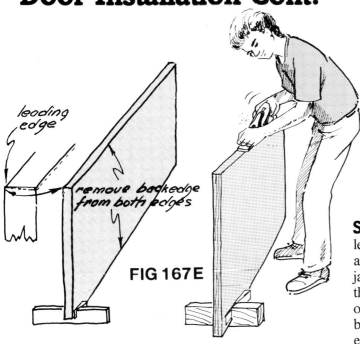

FIG 167E

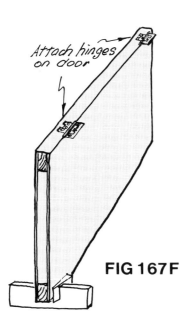

Attach hinges on door

FIG 167F

Step 6 The door is now stood and wedged up beside the opening with the hinges aligning with the previously marked hinge positions on the jamb. (The door should now be in the position as in fig 167G.)
The top screw is now drilled and the screw fixed in place as in figure 167G. Then fix the bottom screw in the bottom hinge. The door is then closed to check that the door and jamb are aligning flush with each other. The remaining screws are then secured.

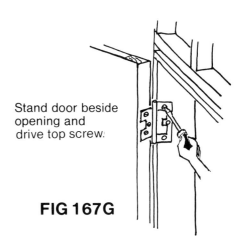

Stand door beside opening and drive top screw.

FIG 167G

Step 7 The lock side jamb is now cut to length. This length is found by closing the door and transferring the door height across on to the jamb. The jamb length will be 3mm higher than the door. The lock side jamb can now be packed out and nailed into position. Allow a 2mm gap between jamb and door. Ensure that the jamb edges are aligning with the face of the door from top to bottom and also flush with wall linings. It is good practice to use pairs of wedges on this jamb to enable easier aligning of the jamb. Where the gap between the door and jamb is too great, the wedges can be simply driven further in. See figure 167H.

Step 8 The head jamb is now cut to length and installed. Wedges are driven in each side until the head fits tightly and nails can be driven down from the top of the head jambs into the side jambs. A pair of wedges or packers are then fitted in the centre and the head jamb and secured. The door is now ready to receive door stops and latchsets or locksets.

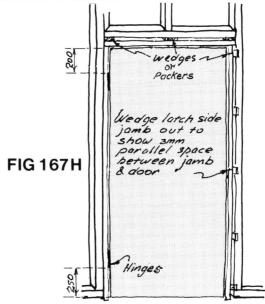

FIG 167H

Hint

Check the door for warp before hanging. Check that the lock side of the door is on the correct side before fitting hinges. The lockside has a block inside the door for installing the lock.

Door Handles & Latchsets

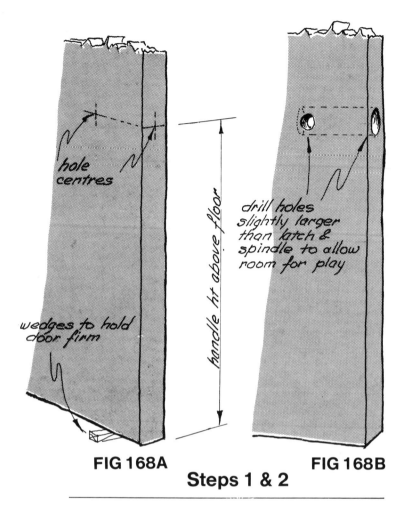

FIG 168A

FIG 168B

Steps 1 & 2

hole centres

wedges to hold door firm

handle ht above floor

drill holes slightly larger than latch & spindle to allow room for play

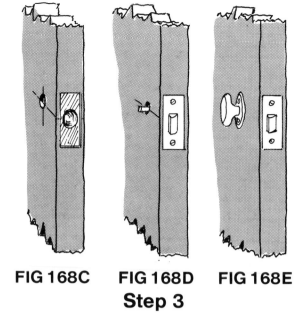

FIG 168C　　**FIG 168D**　　**FIG 168E**

Step 3

Latchsets and snibsets are normally fitted to internal doors: locksets to external or security doors. Installation instructions usually accompany the fittings.

Steps to Installing Door Locks and Latchsets

Step 1　Slide wedges under the door to keep it firm then square a line at the desired latch height on the door edge and continuing across both sides of the door to the handle position. A cardboard template should be provided with the latch set kit. Hold this template on the line and mark the hole centres for the latch and handle mechanism. See Fig. 168A

Step 2　Drill the 2 holes using the drill bit sizes specified on the template. See Fig. 168B If the latch is a mortice lock then a series of holes should be drilled, one directly above the other. A chisel will be required to remove any obstructing wood which prevents a loose installation of the latch casing.

Step 3　To rebate the edge of the door to accept the latch face, install the latch, accurately mark the outer edges of the latch face on the door edge, ensuring it is centrally located. Using a sharp chisel, rebate to the depth of the latch face and screw the latch in place. If the latch bolt does not move freely, further chiselling is required in the hole. The latch will have to be removed. See Figs 168C-E

Step 4　Install the striker plate on the jamb by first closing the door and marking the latch bolt position on the jamb. Hold the striker plate on this position and mark around the bolt housing, ensuring that when the door is closed it will align flush with the jambs. Drill and chisel out the bolt housing then refit the striker plate and mark its surround. Rebate this area for the plate to fit flush with the jamb. Then secure the plate. See Figs 168F-H If this is a new door and jamb, the door stops can now be attached.

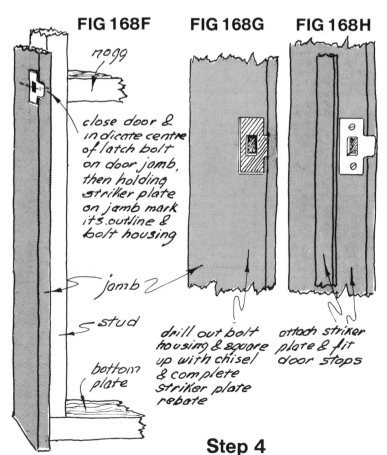

FIG 168F　　**FIG 168G**　　**FIG 168H**

Step 4

nogg

close door & indicate centre of latch bolt on door jamb, then holding striker plate on jamb mark its outline & bolt housing

jamb

stud

bottom plate

drill out bolt housing & square up with chisel & complete striker plate rebate

attach striker plate & fit door stops

Exterior Doors

(See also HSOB page 37)

Exterior doors may open in or out. The latter offers superior weather protection, although this is usually unsuitable for front door use. Entries to front doors should have some form of roof covering to protect the waiting visitor from rain and the door from weather damage. If front doors are stain finished, they will require regular maintenance. Ensure all joints to the frame perimeter have been adequately caulked. Ensure threshholds are at least 20mm below the house floor and falling away.

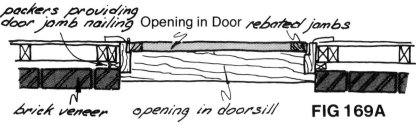

FIG 169A

In brick veneer, exterior doors are installed prior to constructing the brick veneer wall.

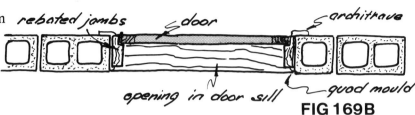

FIG 169B

When block walls are lined inside with plasterboard etc., the jambs are increased in width to finish flush with the linings.

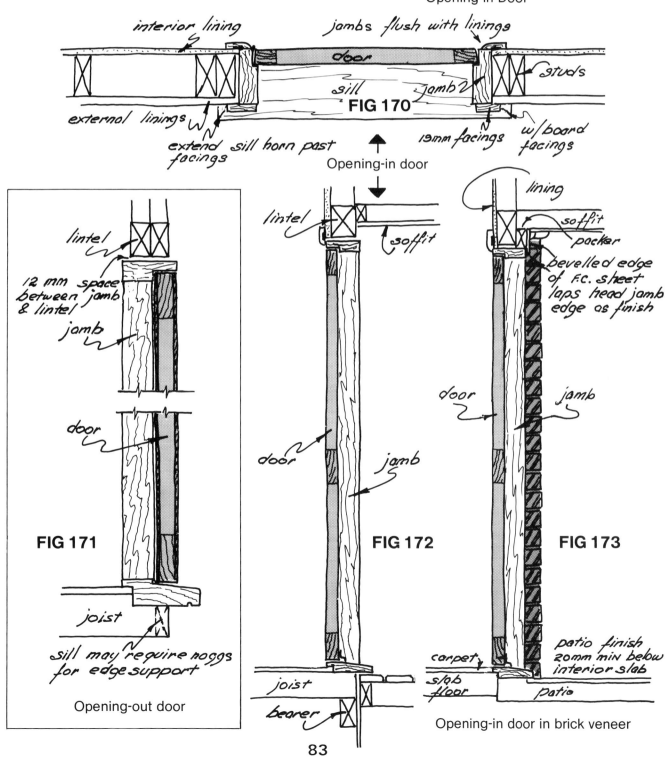

FIG 170

FIG 171

Opening-out door

FIG 172

FIG 173

Opening-in door in brick veneer

83

Plasterboard Lining (Refer to Manufacturer's instructions)

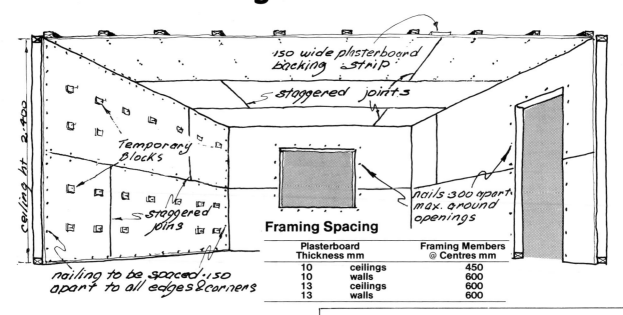

150 wide plasterboard backing strip

staggered joints

Temporary Blocks

staggered joins

ceiling ht 2.400

nailing to be spaced 150 apart to all edges & corners

nails 300 apart max. around openings

Framing Spacing

Plasterboard Thickness mm		Framing Members @ Centres mm
10	ceilings	450
10	walls	600
13	ceilings	600
13	walls	600

Fixing Plasterboard to Walls

Ensure all studs and noggs are flush with plates and that badly bowed studs have been straightened. see page 79.

Fastening

Plasterboard may be fastened to frames by nails or screws or a combination of nails and adhesive. The latter being the most common, is described in this text. Firstly, cut the sheet to fit across the stud frame horizontally, starting with the upper sheet first. Then apply plasterboard stud adhesive to form walnut sized blobs at approximately 225mm centres and starting 200mm in from the edges of the sheets. Then press the sheet firmly in position and nail edges, corners and butt end joins at 150mm centres approximately 12mm in from the sheet edges. Nail at 300mm centres around openings. Drive nails just below the surface without fracturing the linerboard. Hold sheets against studs for 24 hours by nails driven through temporary plasterboard blocks. See figure 175B. Keep temporary nails away from adhesive points.
Nail size: For 10mm and 13mm sheets, use 30mm nails for hardwood and 40mm nails for softwood.

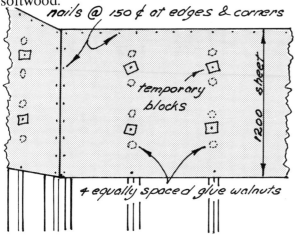

nails @ 150 ¢ at edges & corners

temporary blocks

1200 sheet

4 equally spaced glue walnuts

FIG 175A   Glueing & Nailing Positions

Cutting Plasterboard

Mark the sheet to length required. Hold a straight edge along the line and score through the face with a stanley knife as shown in figure 174A Lift the sheet up and snap the offcut away from the scored face. See figure 174B: then cut the back linerboard see figure 174C. For double plane cuts, as required around openings, make one cut with the saw, then make the intersecting cut as described above. Although fixing of plasterboard is relatively uncomplicated, it is advisable to employ a plasterboard finisher to stop (i.e. plaster) all joints and nail heads.

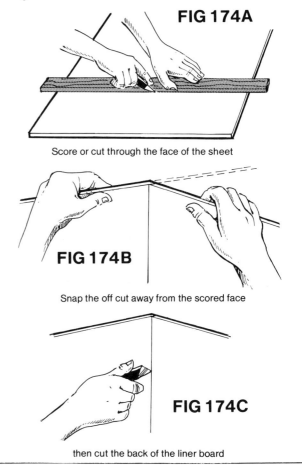

FIG 174A

Score or cut through the face of the sheet

FIG 174B

Snap the off cut away from the scored face

FIG 174C

then cut the back of the liner board

Plasterboard Lining Cont.

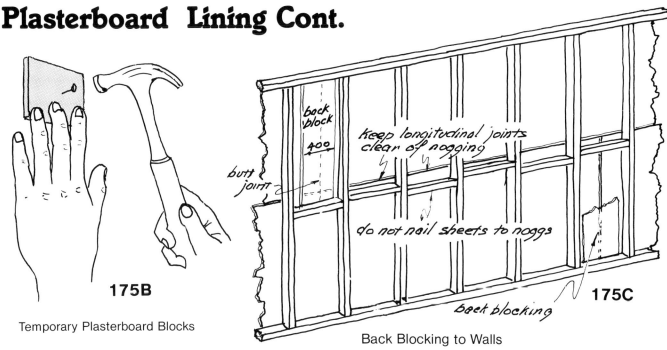

175B

Temporary Plasterboard Blocks

175C

Back Blocking to Walls

Installation of Ceilings

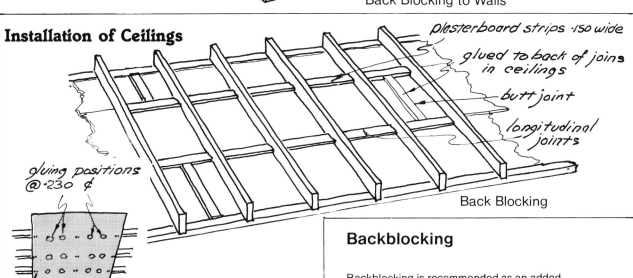

Back Blocking

Apply walnuts of plasterboard adhesive to ceiling joists or battens at 225mm centres maximum and 200mm away from sheet edges. Attach plasterboard with paper bound edges at right angles to ceiling framing. Nail recessed edge to each batten or joists and 200mm away from adhesive points. Nail ends of sheets at butt joints and around service openings at 150mm centres. At cornice line, nail ends of sheets at 300mm centres. Nail the centre of sheets with 2 nails 50mm-75mm apart.

Hold board firmly against joists with temporary blocks and nails as in figure 175B. Remove blocks and nails after 24 hours. Under slow drying conditions, blocks should be left in place for at least 48 hours.

Note

"Walnuts" of adhesive must never coincide with nailing points.
For more detailed information, refer to Manufacturer's leaflets.

Backblocking

Backblocking is recommended as an added precaution against cracking to longitudinal ceiling joints and end joints in ceilings and walls.

Backblocking End Joints in Walls and Ceilings

End or butt joins are made between framing members, not on them. A 400mm minimum strip of plasterboard is cut and glued to the back of joins as in figures 176A or B and 175C. The strip is positioned centrally.

Backblocking Longitudinal Ceiling Joints

Cut strips of plasterboard 150mm wide to fit between joists or battens and glue into position using cornice adhesive. Refer to Manufacturer's instructions for more detailed information.

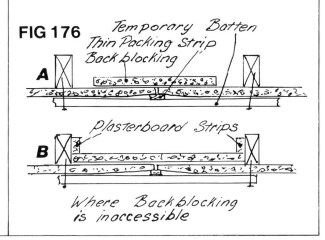

FIG 176

Bath Installation

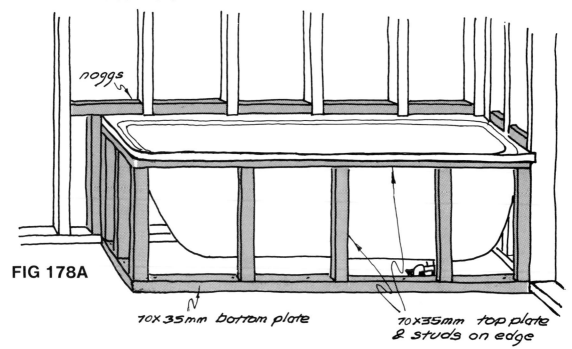

FIG 178A

70 X 35 mm bottom plate

70 X 35 mm top plate & studs on edge

Fitting a Bath

Fitting a bath is a relatively simple operation. First of all, decide on the height preferred for the top edge. This is usually between 450mm and 600mm. If tiles are applied to the side, keep bath to even tile height to save cutting tiles. Allow for tiles to slip behind bath lip.

Step 2 Nogg between the studs above notching to provide a fixing base for the bottom edge of wall linings.

Step 3 Slide bath into housing and construct the supporting walls out of 70mm x 35mm stock on edge. Keep framework back sufficiently from bath lip to allow for lining to slide behind lip.
Bath sides are usually lined with 6mm thick versilux, then tiled: or decorative laminated panelling applied.

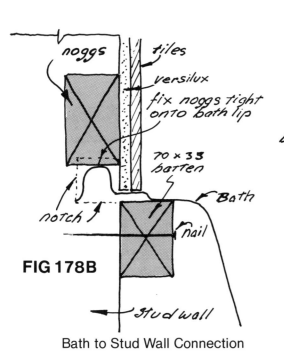

FIG 178B

noggs
tiles
versilux
fix noggs tight onto bath lip
70 x 35 batten
Bath
notch
nail
stud wall

Bath to Stud Wall Connection

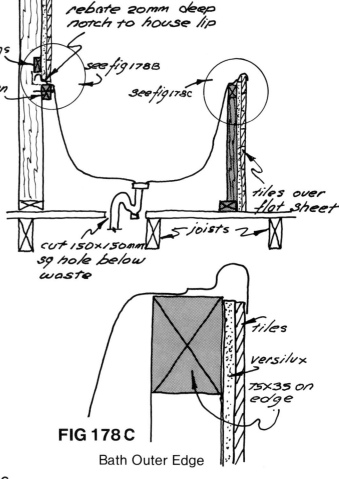

rebate 20mm deep notch to house lip
noggs
batten
see fig 178B
see fig 178C
tiles over flat sheet
cut 150 x 150mm sq hole below waste
joists

FIG 178 C

tiles
versilux
75 X 35 on edge

Bath Outer Edge

Step 1 Cut a hole in the floor directly below the bath waste 150mm x 150mm for plumber to connect waste pipes later. Then on the wall sides of the bath, mark a level line indicating the bath edge. See figure 178B. Notch out the studs to the depth and thickness of the bath lip. Allow for wall sheeting to slide past lip on to the bath.
Then attach a 70mm x 35mm batten on the studs along the level line. See figure 178B.

86

Shower Bases & Trays

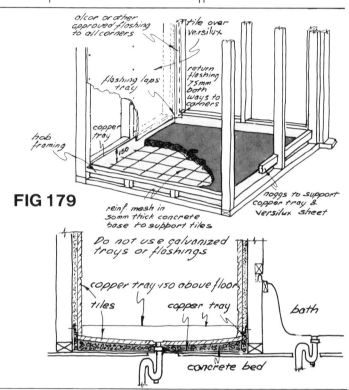

Step Down Shower Base on a Concrete Floor

It is important in this type of installation that Alcor or similarly approved flashings are fitted as illustrated to prevent moisture from gaining access to the timber frame. However, copper trays installed with 150mm high sides are preferred.

Tiled Shower Base on Timber Floor

Step 1 A copper tray should be laid on the timber floor to prevent moisture penetrating the timber floor or walls. When the walls are tiled, 6mm versilux sheeting is laid over the stud walls and carried over the sides of the copper tray, terminating 10mm above the proposed tile surface. Vertical internal corners should have Alcor or approved flashings fitted to them returning 75mm each way and taken down to overlap the copper tray. Do not use galvanized corners or galvanized trays.

Step 2 The shower waste is now fitted into position and the concrete bed laid with reinforcing mesh included. See figure 179. Tiling can then be commenced.

FIG 179

Installing a Prefabricated Shower Base

Such as marble, porcelain, enamel or stainless steel.

Important
Have the base on site to enable accurate positioning of shower partitions. The edges of shower bases should be recessed into the stud wall the same as for bath lips. This prevents water penetrating the stud wall.

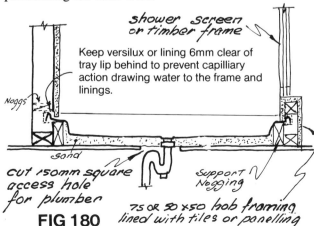

Keep versilux or lining 6mm clear of tray lip behind to prevent capilliary action drawing water to the frame and linings.

FIG 180

Step 1 Mark a level line on the studs surrounding the base and indicating the top edge of the base. Then mark another line below the first indicating the lower edge of the base lip. The studs will be notched out between these lines to receive the base edge or lip. If the base is on a concrete or second storey floor, the base must be raised off the floor suficiently for the plumber to gain access to the trap. An access panel can be placed in front of the shower tray.

Step 2 Notch out the studs to receive the tray lip sufficiently enough to allow the wall sheeting to pass the tray lip with a 6mm clearance to prevent capilliary action. See figure 180.

Step 3 Fit noggs to perimeter of tray as a nailing base for wall sheets.

Step 4 Fit base support for the tray to bed firmly into such as: shaped timber, polystyrene base supplied with the tray: or sand. Slide base into position.

Step 5 Build hob in front of the base similiar to the illustration in figure 179.
The shower is now ready to receive linings.

Architraves

Door and Window Architraves

Architraves are mitre cut and mitre butt joined, glued together and nailed to wall framing on one side: door jambs or window reveals on their opposite side. On doors, the bottom end of the side architraves are cut square first.

How to Fit Architraves

Ensure linings are flush or slightly back from jambs or reveals.

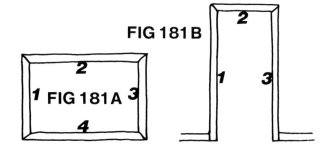

FIG 181B

1 FIG 181A 3

Step 1 Cut a 45 degree mitre on one end of architrave No.1. See figure 181A. Then holding the architrave in its proposed position, mark its opposite end. Hold the bottom corner of the mitre 2mm past the jamb or reveal as in figure 182A. Allowing the same 2mm quirk on the opposite end, mark and cut this first architrave and tack in position. Fix each end first then tack the centres maintaining a 2mm parallel quirk. With a little practice, this quirk is maintained by the eye.

Step 2 Mitre one end of architrave 2 and hold this architrave in position mitre to mitre. Mark and cut the opposite end and tack in position. Remember to glue the mitre joint. Using this procedure, fit the remaining architraves. When encountering a mitre that is not tight, lightly dress the loose mitre until it fits, slightly undercutting the end grain using a plane. Architraves should be sanded prior to fitting.

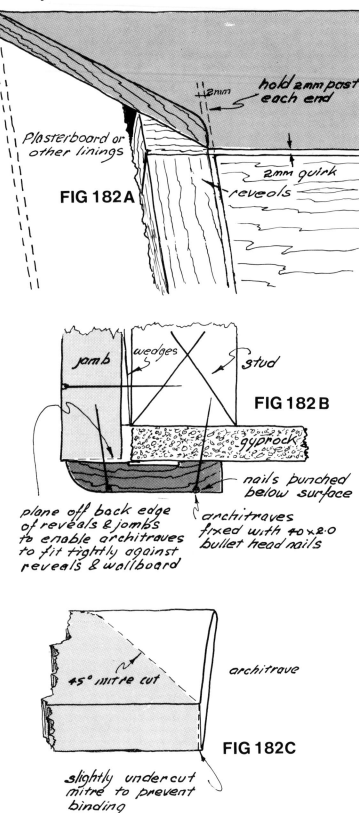

Plasterboard or other linings

hold 2mm past each end

2mm quirk reveals

FIG 182A

jamb — wedges — stud

FIG 182B

gyprock

nails punched below surface

plane off back edge of reveals & jombs to enable architraves to fit tightly against reveals & wallboard

architraves fixed with 40×2·0 bullet head nails

45° mitre cut

architrave

FIG 182C

slightly undercut mitre to prevent binding

Awkward Situations

Where doorways and windows are close to walls, architraves are permitted to be ripped down to fit the narrow space. See figure 183A Where this space is 10mm-20mm wider than the architrave, a wider architrave is used. See figure 183B. This simplifies wallpapering and painting and looks tidier.

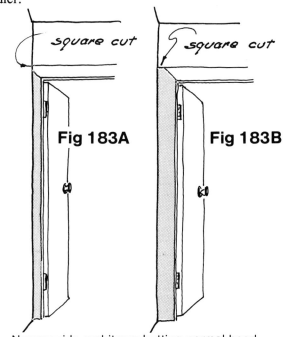

square cut

square cut

Fig 183A

Fig 183B

Narrow side architrave butting normal head architrave necessitates square cutting part of the end of the head architrave. Wide side architraves butting normal head architrave necessitates square cutting part of the top of the side architrave.

Skirtings

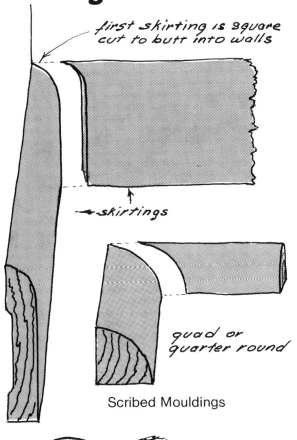

first skirting is square cut to butt into walls

← skirtings

quad or quarter round

Scribed Mouldings

Skirting

Internal corners of skirting are not mitred but scribed to fit the contour of the previously fitted mouldings.

How to Scribe and Cut Skirtings and Similarly Curved Mouldings

To obtain skirting lengths, use a tape measure.

Step 1   First moulding is square cut to fit tightly between opening and wall as in fig 184D.

Step 2   Second moulding is scribed to fit the contour of the first moulding by first cutting a mitre as in figure 184B. Then with a coping saw, remove all the end grain wood slightly undercutting. See figure 184C. Then cut the skirting to length, applying the square cut to the opposite end. Ensure a tight fit. When nailing skirtings, ensure the top edge is nailed to the studs.

Step 3   Continue fitting the remaining mouldings as described . External corners are   mitre joined.

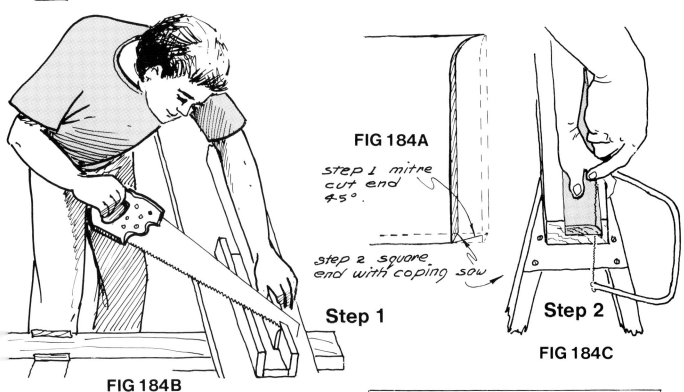

FIG 184A

step 1 mitre cut end 45°.

step 2 square end with coping saw

Step 1

Step 2

FIG 184B

FIG 184C

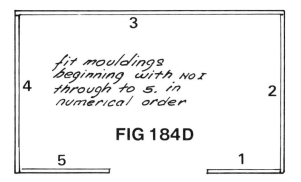

3

fit mouldings beginning with NO 1 through to 5. in numerical order

4   2

FIG 184D

5   1

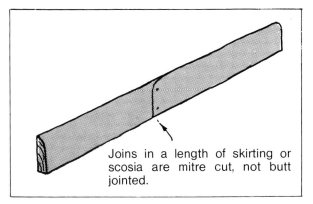

Joins in a length of skirting or scosia are mitre cut, not butt jointed.

Kitchen Cupboards

Constructing kitchen cabinets is not beyond the capabilities of the handyman. Premade doors and drawers are available. Doors can either be flush fitting or overlapping. Flush fitting doors are hinged inside and flush with the face of the cabinet exposing the mullions. When constructing cabinets to house flush fitting doors, perpendicular mullions are attached to the face of the cabinets. Doors are hung to hide the end grain of the bottom shelf. Overlapping doors are hung outside the cabinet front hiding most of the cabinet except for narrow gaps between doors. This method is the most popularly applied today and is the type used in figure 185.

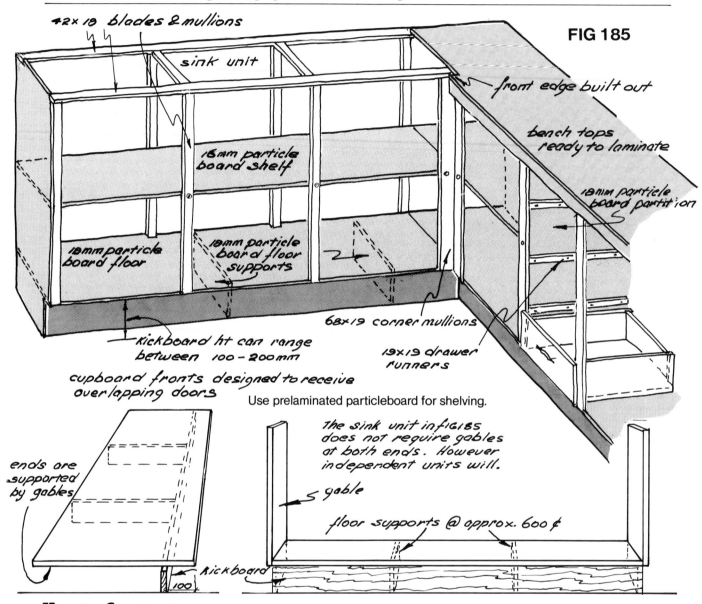

FIG 185

42x19 blades & mullions

sink unit

front edge built out

bench tops ready to laminate

18mm particle board shelf

18mm particle board partition

18mm particle board floor

18mm particle board floor supports

68x19 corner mullions

19x19 drawer runners

kickboard ht can range between 100 - 200mm

cupboard fronts designed to receive overlapping doors

Use prelaminated particleboard for shelving.

ends are supported by gables

the sink unit in fig 185 does not require gables at both ends. However independent units will.

gable

floor supports @ approx. 600 ∅

kickboard

100

How to Construct

Step 1 Construct kickboard and floor using 18mm particle board. Kickboards are usually 100mm deep and can be from 150mm-200m high. Cut supports for the back edge of the floor (called floor supports in the illustration) and the same height as kickboard. Glue and nail floor to kickboard and floor supports. Floor supports are indicated by dotted lines.

Step 2 Cut gable ends out of 16mm particle board. Allow extra depth for kickboard to run past end grain of gable. The floor will butt into the gable end.

Step 3 Attach gable ends to floor and kickboard, glueing and nailing.

Step 4 Attach shelf supports to gable ends and erect 42mmx19mm perpendicular mullions with 42mmx19mm bench top blades to support mullions. Bottom ends are rebated into cupboard floor. Mullions are spaced to suit doors.

Step 5 Fit cross runners to support intermediate shelf and attach shelf. Shelf can fit inside mullions.

Step 6 Fit bench top: 18mm particle board can be used. Benchtops usually overlap cabinets and the overlap thickened with particle board or dressed wood. Surface is then laminated.

Step 7 Fit and hang doors using appropriate hinges.

90

Kitchen Cupboards Cont.

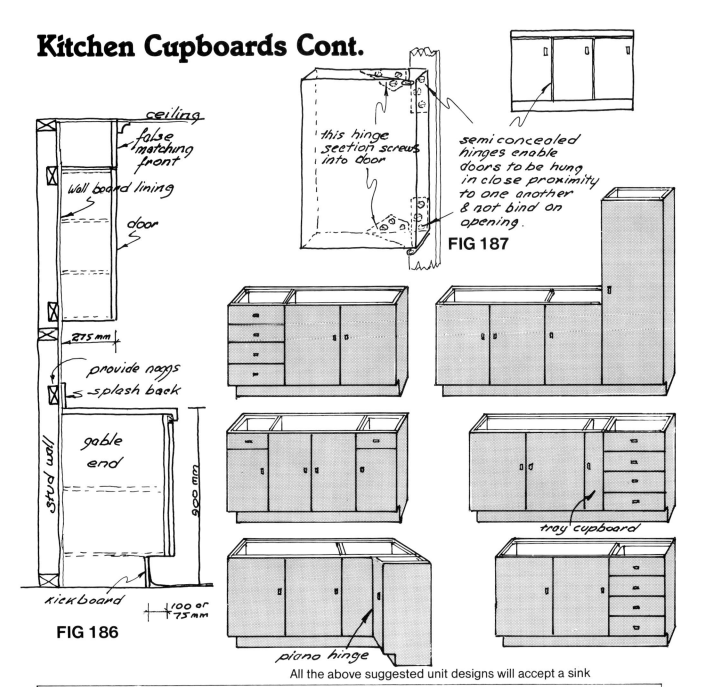

FIG 186

FIG 187

this hinge section screws into door

semi concealed hinges enable doors to be hung in close proximity to one another & not bind on opening.

ceiling
false matching front
Wall board lining
door
275 mm
provide nogs
splash back
gable end
stud wall
900 mm
kickboard
100 or 75 mm

tray cupboard

piano hinge

All the above suggested unit designs will accept a sink

Drawers

Step 1 Measure and divide opening height up into drawer spacings. Mark position of drawer runners. Work from the top making allowance for the overlapping of drawer faces. If a bottom drawer is not required, a false front and handle can be attached to the cabinet.

Step 2 Drawer sides and fronts are squared and cut to length and given a groove or slot to house the bottom, usually 4mm hardboard. Sides of drawers have a slot across the back end to house the back leaf. See figure 188.

Step 3 Cut back leaf and the bottom. Assemble the drawer using glue and nails.

Step 4 Drawer face is now cut and attached. Glue and screw from the inside.

Step 5 Runners are now attached at the appropriate spacings. Blocks are fitted to prevent drawers from falling out when fully extended.

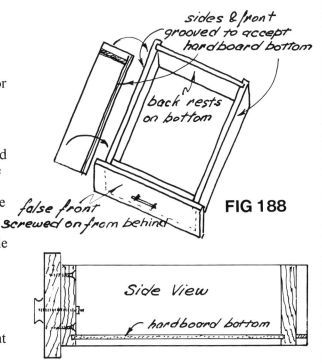

sides & front grooved to accept hardboard bottom

back rests on bottom

false front screwed on from behind

FIG 188

Side View

hardboard bottom

7

Brick Veneer, Cavity Brick & Concrete Block Details

Brick Veneer Details

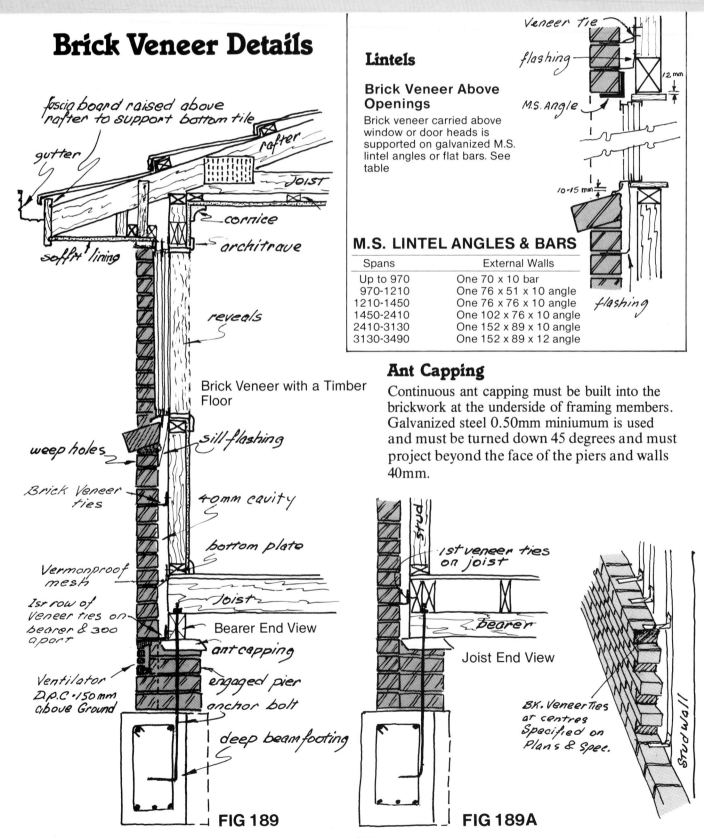

Lintels

Brick Veneer Above Openings

Brick veneer carried above window or door heads is supported on galvanized M.S. lintel angles or flat bars. See table

M.S. LINTEL ANGLES & BARS

Spans	External Walls
Up to 970	One 70 x 10 bar
970-1210	One 76 x 51 x 10 angle
1210-1450	One 76 x 76 x 10 angle
1450-2410	One 102 x 76 x 10 angle
2410-3130	One 152 x 89 x 10 angle
3130-3490	One 152 x 89 x 12 angle

Ant Capping

Continuous ant capping must be built into the brickwork at the underside of framing members. Galvanized steel 0.50mm miniumum is used and must be turned down 45 degrees and must project beyond the face of the piers and walls 40mm.

Brick Veneer with a Timber Floor

Bearer End View

Joist End View

FIG 189

FIG 189A

Brick Veneer Details Cont.

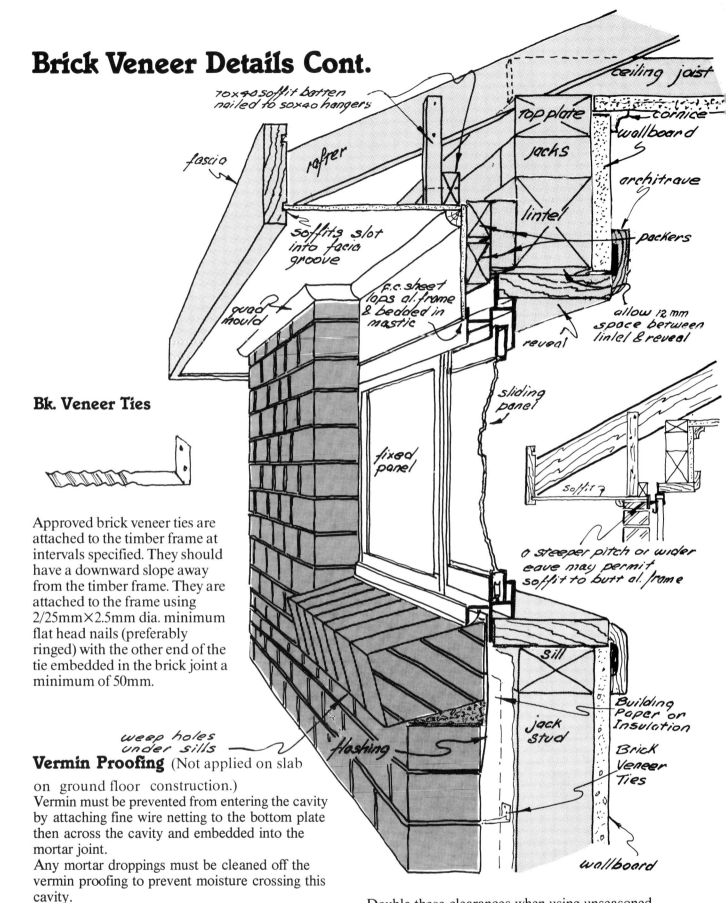

70x40 soffit batten nailed to 50x40 hangers

fascia

rafter

soffits slot into facia groove

quad mould

f.c. sheet laps al. frame & bedded in mastic

ceiling joist

top plate

jacks

cornice

wallboard

architrave

lintel

packers

allow 12 mm space between lintel & reveal

reveal

sliding panel

fixed panel

a steeper pitch or wider eave may permit soffit to butt al. frame

soffit ?

weep holes under sills

flashing

sill

jack Stud

Building Paper or Insulation

Brick Veneer Ties

wallboard

Bk. Veneer Ties

Approved brick veneer ties are attached to the timber frame at intervals specified. They should have a downward slope away from the timber frame. They are attached to the frame using 2/25mm×2.5mm dia. minimum flat head nails (preferably ringed) with the other end of the tie embedded in the brick joint a minimum of 50mm.

Vermin Proofing (Not applied on slab on ground floor construction.)

Vermin must be prevented from entering the cavity by attaching fine wire netting to the bottom plate then across the cavity and embedded into the mortar joint.
Any mortar droppings must be cleaned off the vermin proofing to prevent moisture crossing this cavity.

Shrinkage

A space allowance for the timber wall frames to shrink must be provided at the following two points:
A.   5mm between brick sills and window frames on the lower storey or single storey houses and 10mm on the second storey.
B.   8mm between top brick coarse and soffits on single storey houses and 12mm on the 2nd storey.

Double these clearances when using unseasoned hardwood.
For further information on brick veneer refer to index.

Hint

If the brick veneer or block walls continue up into the soffits, it is advisable when ordering the base bricks to include the total brick requirement for the whole house. Variations in colour can occur when ordering separate lots.

Concrete Block Estimating

For further and more comprehensive instruction on block masonry construction, see HSOB pages 58-65.)

Important

Keep blocks dry on site. At the end of each day's work, cover walls to prevent moisture entering the block cores.

Volume of Grout Required to Fill Cores

Blocks Type	Vol to fill 100 blocks
2001	.66 of a cubic metre

No. of blocks filled using 1 cu metre   151

(200 Series Single Leaf)

■ HORIZONTAL   ■ VERTICAL

BLOCKS REQ.	FULL BLOCK LENGTH MET	PLUS ¼ Block MET	PLUS ½ Block MET	PLUS ¾ Block MET	200mm High Block Courses	Height –M–
1	0.4	0.5	0.6	0.7	1	0.2
2	0.8	0.9	1.0	1.1	2	0.4
3	1.2	1.3	1.4	1.5	3	0.6
4	1.6	1.7	1.8	1.9	4	0.8
5	2.0	2.1	2.2	2.3	5	1.0
6	2.4	2.5	2.6	2.7	6	1.2
7	2.8	2.9	3.0	3.1	7	1.4
8	3.2	3.3	3.4	3.5	8	1.6
9	3.6	3.7	3.8	3.9	9	1.8
10	4.0	4.1	4.2	4.3	10	2.0
11	4.4	4.5	4.6	4.7	11	2.2
12	4.8	4.9	5.0	5.1	12	2.4
13	5.2	5.3	5.4	5.5	13	2.6
14	5.6	5.7	5.8	5.9	14	2.8
15	6.0	6.1	6.2	6.3	15	3.0
16	6.4	6.5	6.6	6.7	16	3.2
17	6.8	6.9	7.0	7.1	17	3.4
18	7.2	7.3	7.4	7.5	18	3.6
19	7.6	7.7	7.8	7.9	19	3.8
20	8.0	8.1	7.2	8.3	20	4.0

Quantity of blocks required in a given length of wall is found in the first column (BLOCKS REQ.)

---

200 Series Blocks

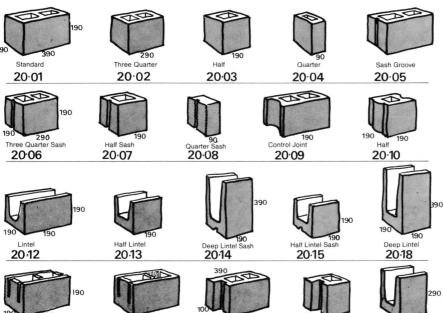

Standard **20·01** | Three Quarter **20·02** | Half **20·03** | Quarter **20·04** | Sash Groove **20·05**

Three Quarter Sash **20·06** | Half Sash **20·07** | Quarter Sash **20·08** | Control Joint **20·09** | Half **20·10**

Lintel **20·12** | Half Lintel **20·13** | Deep Lintel Sash **20·14** | Half Lintel Sash **20·15** | Deep Lintel **20·18**

Knockout Bond Beam **20·20** | Corner **20·21** | Full Jamb **20·23** | Half Jamb **20·24** | Three Quarter Lintel **20·25**

Sash **20·26** | Solid **20·31** | Sill (Full Height) **20·37** | Sill (Half Height) **20·38** | Channel **20·42**

"H" Block **20·48** | Pilaster Pilaster **20·55 & 20·56** | Three Quarter **20·57** | Bonded Pilaster Half **20·60**

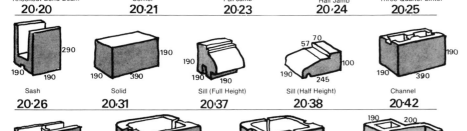

Bonded Pilaster Half **20·61** | Fireblock 3 Hours **20·705** | Fireblock 4 Hours **20·708** | Single Core **20·925** | **20·97**

200mm Half Height

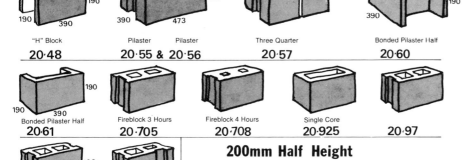

20·98 | **20·99** | Standard **20·71** | **20·72** | **20·73** | Quarter **20·74**

Mortar Mixture

A sugested mortar mixture 1:1:6 e.g. 1 part cement, 1 part hydrated lime and 6 parts block laying sand. For work below DPC level: 1 part cement, ¼ part lime and 3 parts sand.

1 bag of cement will lay between 150–200 blocks.

Control Joints

Control joints should be constructed at intervals not exceeding 10 metres for walls containing bond beams and 7 metre intervals for walls without bond beams. Ensure when plans are drawn that positions of all reinforcing control joints and bond beams are indicated clearly. All block walls and openings must be block module length and height.

Window and Door Fixing

Method A

Before commencing blockwork, establish opening sizes with window supplier. Windows are attached to blocks by screws (through the fins provided at the edges of the frames) screwed into rawl plugs placed in the blockwork.

Method B

Windows are installed as work progresses. See HSOB pages 58-62

Materials Required

1. Blocks
2. Cement
3. Blocklaying sand
4. Hydrated lime
5. Reinforcing rods & starter rods
6. Plasticiser
7. Grout
8. D.P.C.

Concrete Block

Block walls are 'green' when freshly laid and walls are most vulnerable to bumps by careless handling of scaffolding, wheelbarrows etc.
200mm thick block walls used as the sole external walls are referred to as single leaf masonry walls. Special attention must be paid to waterproofing block walls. One simple Manufacturer's recommendation is the application of three coats of 100% acrylic paint ensuring that each coat is meticulously applied according to Manufacturer's instructions. For this reason, downpipes and any other wall fixtures should be attached after painting.

Laying

The principals of laying, levelling and lining blocks true is the same as for brickwork. See pages 105-107. Blocks should be kept dry on the site.

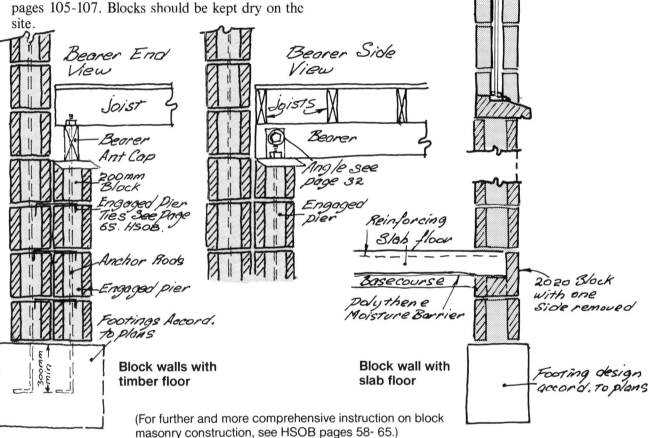

FIG 193

Block walls with timber floor

Block wall with slab floor

(For further and more comprehensive instruction on block masonry construction, see HSOB pages 58- 65.)

Fixing Linings to Blockwork

See figure 194 This is the most commonly applied method when plasterboard is being used. If the wall is straight and flat without serious hollows, the board is glued directly to the wall using the Manufacturer's recommended adhesive and glueing positions. Manufacturers have instruction literature available for this application.

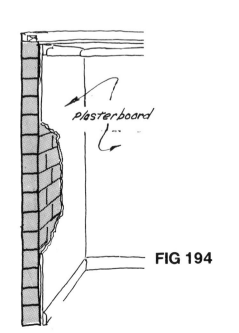

FIG 194

Cavity Brick Details

Damp Proof Courses

A damp proof course must be provided 150mm above finished ground level or paving.

Cavity Flashings

Flashings should be built into brick joints crossing the cavity above openings (see figure 195C) and weep holes provided on these flashings at 700mm centres maximum. Flashings should be provided above lintels and below sills. For more information on cavity brick, see HSOB pages 51-57.

Hint

Spray a protective coating of RP7 on aluminium frames and glass before cement droppings come into contact to prevent cement staining.

Lintels & Brickwork Over Openings

Galvanized angles or bars are fitted to support brickwork which continues above openings in brick walls. One angle or bar is used in each brick leaf. The long side of angles extends vertically up the cavity. The ends of angles or bars should have a minimum of 110mm bearing at each end for openings up to 1800mm wide and 225mm for openings over 1800mm wide.

M.S. LINTEL ANGLES & ARCH BARS

Spans	External Walls	Internal Walls
Up to 970	One 70 x 10 bar	One 70 x 10 bar
970-1210	One 76 x 51 x 10 angle	One 76 x 51 x 10 angle
1210-1450	One 76 x 76 x 10 angle	One 76 x 51 x 10 angle
1450-2410	One 102 x 76 x 10 angle	Two 64 x 51 x 8 angles
2410-3130	One 152 x 89 x 10 angle	Two 89 x 64 x 10 angles
3130-3490	One 152 x 89 x 12 angle	–

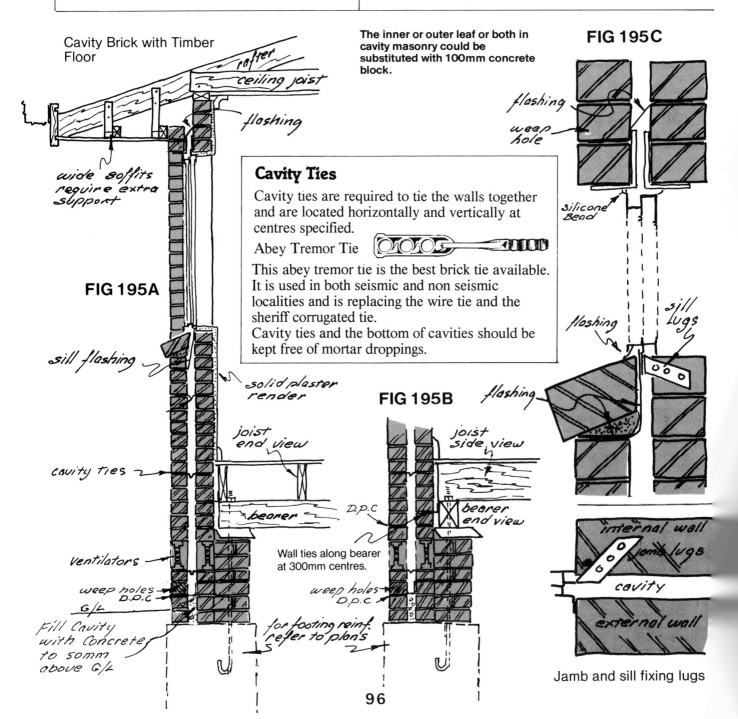

Cavity Brick with Timber Floor

rafter
ceiling joist
flashing

wide soffits require extra support

FIG 195A

sill flashing

solid plaster render

Cavity Ties

Cavity ties are required to tie the walls together and are located horizontally and vertically at centres specified.

Abey Tremor Tie

This abey tremor tie is the best brick tie available. It is used in both seismic and non seismic localities and is replacing the wire tie and the sheriff corrugated tie.

Cavity ties and the bottom of cavities should be kept free of mortar droppings.

cavity ties

joist end view

bearer

ventilators

weep holes D.P.C
G/L

Fill Cavity with Concrete to 50mm above G/L

FIG 195B

joist side view

bearer end view

D.P.C

Wall ties along bearer at 300mm centres.

weep holes D.P.C

for footing reinf. refer to plan's

The inner or outer leaf or both in cavity masonry could be substituted with 100mm concrete block.

FIG 195C

flashing
weep hole

Silicone Bead

flashing

sill lugs

flashing

internal wall
jamb lugs
cavity
external wall

Jamb and sill fixing lugs

Cavity Brick Details

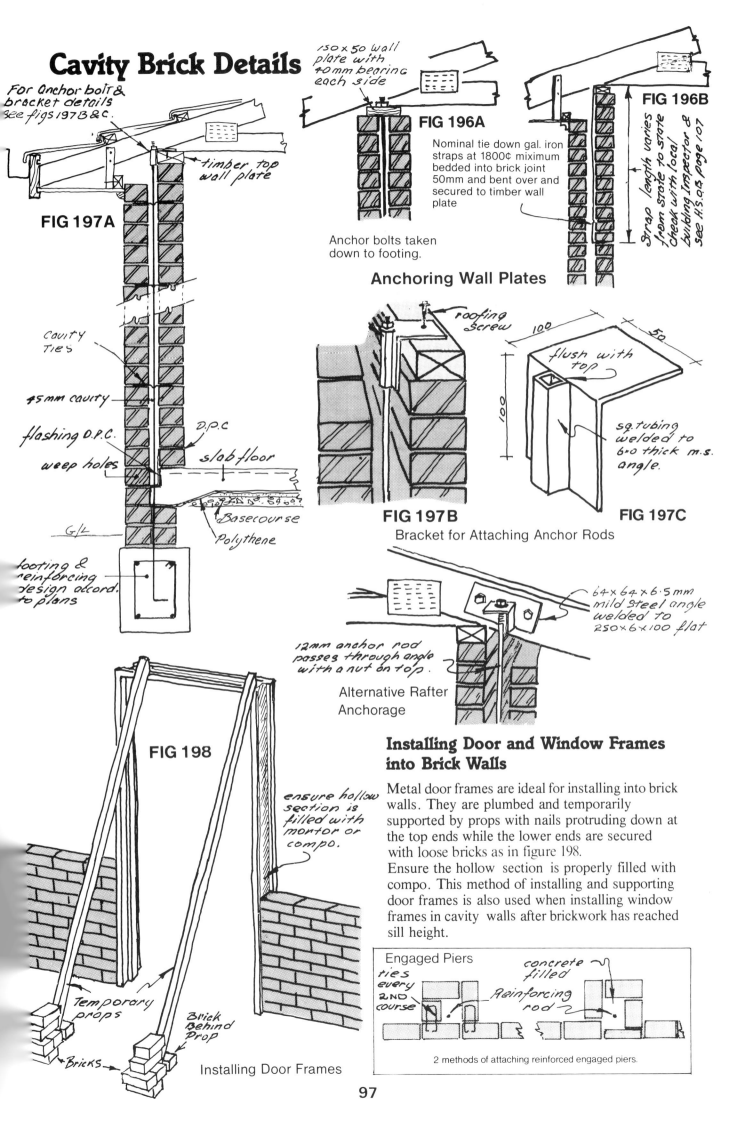

For Anchor bolt & bracket details see figs 197B & C.

FIG 197A

timber top wall plate

cavity ties

45mm cavity

flashing D.P.C.

weep holes

D.P.C

slab floor

G/L

Basecourse

Polythene

footing & reinforcing design accord. to plans

---

150 x 50 wall plate with 40mm bearing each side

FIG 196A

Nominal tie down gal. iron straps at 1800¢ miximum bedded into brick joint 50mm and bent over and secured to timber wall plate

Anchor bolts taken down to footing.

Anchoring Wall Plates

FIG 196B

Strap length varies from state to state Check with local building Inspector & see H.S.a.a page 107

---

roofing screw

FIG 197B

100

50

flush with top

100

sq. tubing welded to 6.0 thick m.s. angle.

FIG 197C

Bracket for Attaching Anchor Rods

---

64 x 64 x 6.5mm mild steel angle welded to 250 x 6 x 100 flat

12mm anchor rod passes through angle with a nut on top.

Alternative Rafter Anchorage

Installing Door and Window Frames into Brick Walls

Metal door frames are ideal for installing into brick walls. They are plumbed and temporarily supported by props with nails protruding down at the top ends while the lower ends are secured with loose bricks as in figure 198.

Ensure the hollow section is properly filled with compo. This method of installing and supporting door frames is also used when installing window frames in cavity walls after brickwork has reached sill height.

FIG 198

ensure hollow section is filled with mortor or compo.

Temporary props

Brick Behind Prop

Bricks

Installing Door Frames

Engaged Piers

ties every 2ND course

concrete filled

Reinforcing rod

2 methods of attaching reinforced engaged piers.

8

Miscellaneous

Plumber

All plumbing work must be carried out by a Registered Plumber. However, some shires will permit stormwater, guttering and downpipes to be erected by unlicenced persons. Enquire at your local Council. Owner Builders can assist the plumber by providing nogging at the positions designated by the plumber.

Stages to Employ the Plumber

1. *Prior to pouring the slab.*
2. *After fascia boards are fitted for the installation of guttering.*
3. *After roof is on but prior to lining walls and before electrician arrives.*
4. *After lining walls to install fittings, P.C. items and general completion.*

It is good practice to liaise with the plumber throughout the job.

Drainer

Two forms of drainage are to be considered.
1. Stormwater
2. Sewerage or septic

All sewerage and septic work must be carried out by an authorized drainer. In many shires, the installation of stormwater can be carried out by unlicenced persons, so enquire.

Stages to Employ a Drainlayer

Laying pipelines should be carried out prior to:-
A. *Constructing any walls close to boundary fences.*
B. *Pouring concrete footings, slabs or drives.*
C. *The Plumber laying waste pipes.*

Ensure excavations for drainage do not expose the house wall or column foundations.

Electrician

All electrical work must be performed by an Authorized Electrician.

Meter box position should be planned in consultation with the Electrical Authority prior to erecting any walls. Consider having underground cables installed before deciding on the meter box position.

The wiring procedure entails:-
The drilling of holes through framework or brickwork to each room. Fixing of switch boxes followed by the laying of cables terminating at switchboxes, switchboards and meter boards.

Stages to Employ Electrician

1. *To install temporary job power pole.*
2. *Prior to pouring slabs if they contain any heating systems or wiring.*
3. *Wiring out – after roof is sheathed but after plumber has installed water pipelines.*
4. *To install fittings and finish off.*

Prior to stage 3, before the electrician arrives, it is good practice to mark on the frame with chalk the desired positions of lights and power points. Take into consideration proposed furniture, 2-way switches and outside lighting positions.

Corrugated Iron Roofing

FIG 202

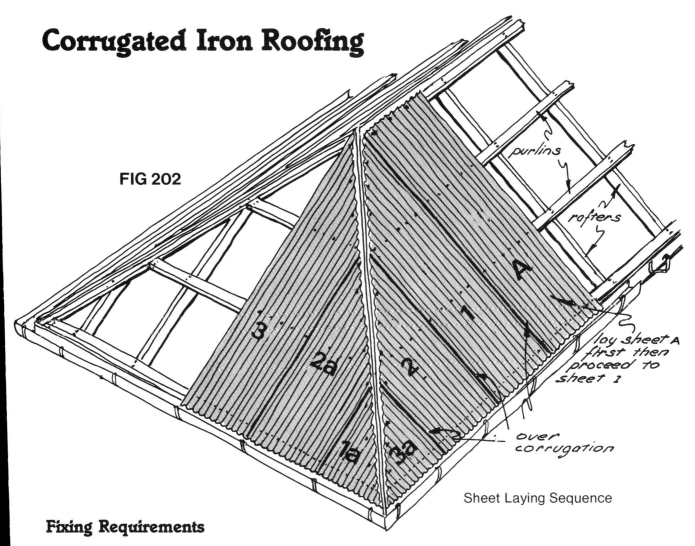

lay sheet A first then proceed to sheet 1

over corrugation

purlins

rafters

Sheet Laying Sequence

Fixing Requirements

Manufacturers literature will specify the correct fixing type and their spacings.

It is advisable to have the plumber carry out hip end roofing. However, where this task must be performed by the builder, use these instructions:

How to Lay Corrugated Iron Roofing for Hip End Roofs

Step 1 Sheet A is laid with the overlapping corrugation towards the hip end and parallel with the rafters. Only tack this sheet top and bottom and allow 50mm minimum overhang into the gutter. The remaining full length sheets may be laid now or delayed until the hip end is completed. To complete hip end, continue to Step 2.

Step 2 Scribe and cut sheet No. 1 to provide sheet 1a and attach in place sliding under sheet A and allowing 1½ laps.

Step 3 Scribe and cut sheet 2 to provide 2a and attach as previously described.

Step 4 Attach sheet 3a in the same manner.

Step 5 Fit the remaining offcuts on the opposite sides of hips (by turning them over) and following the sequence illustrated in figure 202. Top ends of all sheets are weathered by having their hollows turned up All laps should be primed.

barge capping

batten
rafter
bargeboard

FIG 203

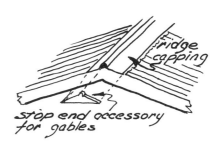

ridge capping

stop end accessory for gables

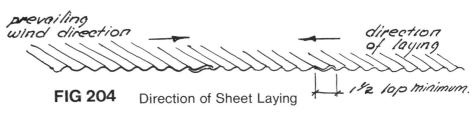

prevailing wind direction

direction of laying

1½ lap minimum.

FIG 204   Direction of Sheet Laying

Flashings

Flashing roofs abutting timber framed walls.

Flashings

Flashings must be installed to ensure not only that water does not enter the interior of the building, but that moisture does not come into continual contact with the timber framework eventually causing dry rot. Where, in future, flashings cannot be easily replaced, it is advisable to use copper or lead. Ensure that the metal in flashings and fixings are compatible with the metal on to which they will be in contact to prevent electrolyses. The illustrated examples cover the most common situations encountered.

method of flashing sloping roofs abutting brick or masonry walls.

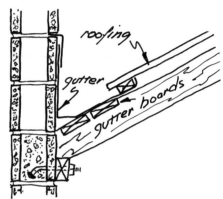

Internal gutters against masonry walls.

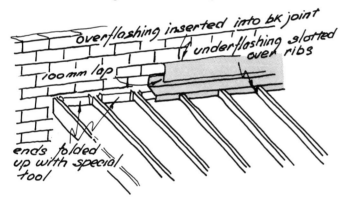

Metal roof decking abutting brick or masonry walls.

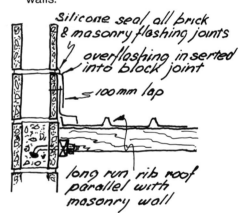

Metal roofing parallel to brick or masonry walls.

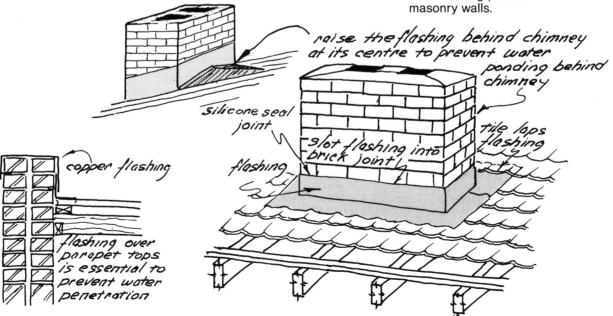

Parapet flashing

Flashing chimneys.

100

Arches in Brickwork

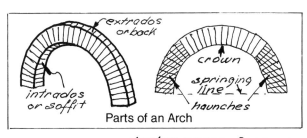

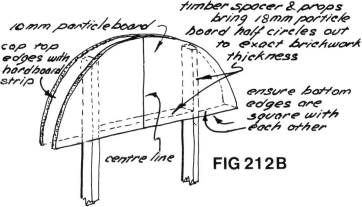

Parts of an Arch

Arch Centres

The arch formwork supporting a brick arch is known as a 'centre'.

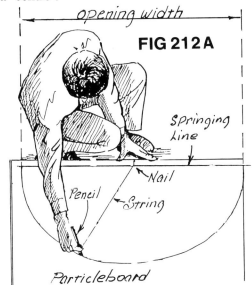

FIG 212A

Makeshift compass with a string attached to a nail at one end & a pencil at the other to form a half circle arch.

How to Contruct Arch Centres

Step 1 Cut two arches out of 18 mm particle board ensuring both are identical. See figure 212A.

FIG 212B

Step 2 Attach timber spacer and props of the required depth to space particle board out to the exact brickwork thickness. See figure 212B.

Step 3 Nail a strip of 3mm hardboard over the curved particle board edges enclosing the space between.

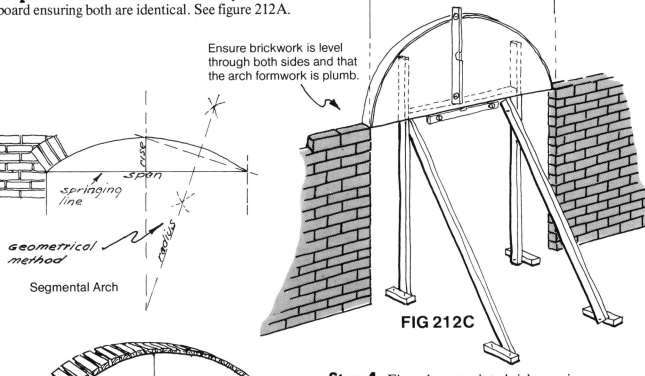

Ensure brickwork is level through both sides and that the arch formwork is plumb.

Segmental Arch

FIG 212C

FIG 212D

Step 4 Fit arch centre into brick opening ensuring it is flush with the brickwork on both sides and that the centreline is plumb. Level centre by packing up either leg. When all is level and plumb, brace and secure as in figure 212C. For brickwork of greater thickness, just increase the depth of the timber props inside the centres with packing. Use battens or double layers of hardboard to cross the space between the centres around the curve. See figure 212D.

101

Arches in Plasterboard

Arches in Plasterboard

Using the manufactured arch beading and applied as described below:

Step 1 Construct archway framework using timber of the required thickness to space apart 13mm particle board arch centres out to existing wall framing thickness.

Step 2 Cut 13mm particle board arch centres as described in figure 212A and nail in place.

Step 3 Hold plasterboard or gyprock over proposed archway and mark the arch profile on the back of the sheet allowing an extra 10mm below particle board centre for fitting soffit. Then, using a knife or keyhole saw, cut out arch. After carrying out this operation on both sides, nail plasterboard arches in place ensuring the 10mm is maintained below particleboard centres all round.

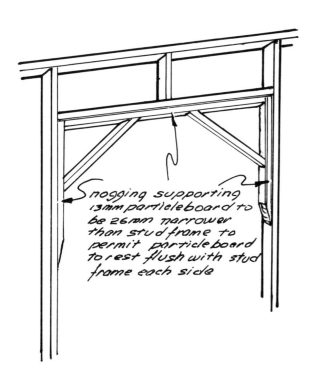

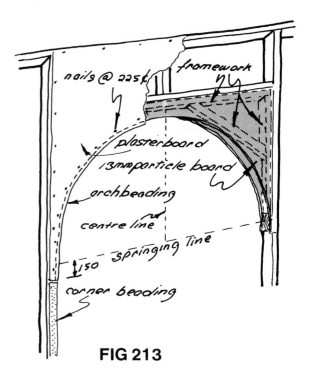

FIG 213

Step 4 Cut soffit strip of plasterboard to fit between the face sheets and attach this soffit by first applying beads of cornice adhesive to the back edges of the particle board centres. Then press soffit into place ensuring that continuous contact has been made. The soffit should be nailed each side of the arch a minimum of 50mm below the springing line.

Step 5 Take the archway beading supplied and preform it to the shape of the constructed arch by moulding it by hand around the 13mm particle-board waste from which the arch was cut out of. Then holding it to the constructed arch, cut it to the

correct length allowing 150mm below the springing line.

Step 6 Fit archway bead to arch with perforated edge on soffit side of arch. Nail to stud no closer than 50mm below springing line. Now using pressure on the opposite side, force bead to fit tightly around arch contour and nail again below springing line on the opposite side.

Step 7 Fit external perforated corner beading to vertical corners below the arch. Now the arch is ready for stopping.

102

Suspended Concrete Patios

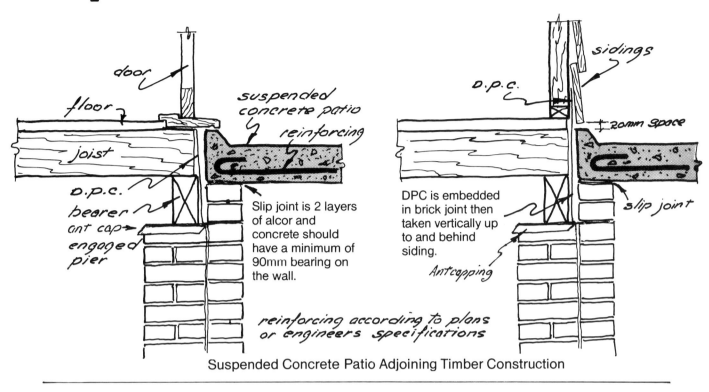

Suspended Concrete Patio Adjoining Timber Construction

How to Construct a Suspended
Concrete Patio *(see fig 215)*

Step 1 Have brick columns constructed and their height terminated directly below the underside of the proposed concrete patio.

Step 2 Erect bearers on top of scaffolding jacks or 100mm x 100mm timber toms and brace both ways. Secure 100mm x 50mm support joists and lay sheet form work. Cut sheets to fit neatly around columns. Nail edge formwork to the flat sheet decking formwork. Fit edge chocks to prevent overturning or bulging while concrete is being poured.

Step 3 Place floor reinforcing mesh, then fit anchor rods into brick columns and bend and tie into mesh. Steel sizes and quantities can be obtained from plans or specifications.

Step 4 Pour concrete and remove formwork after 14 days or according to specifications.

FIG 214

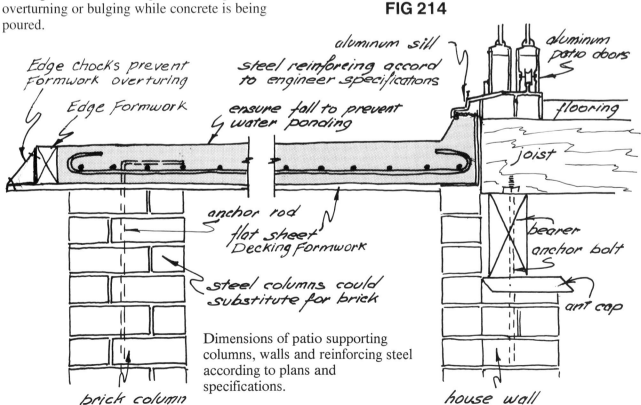

Suspended Concrete Patios Cont.

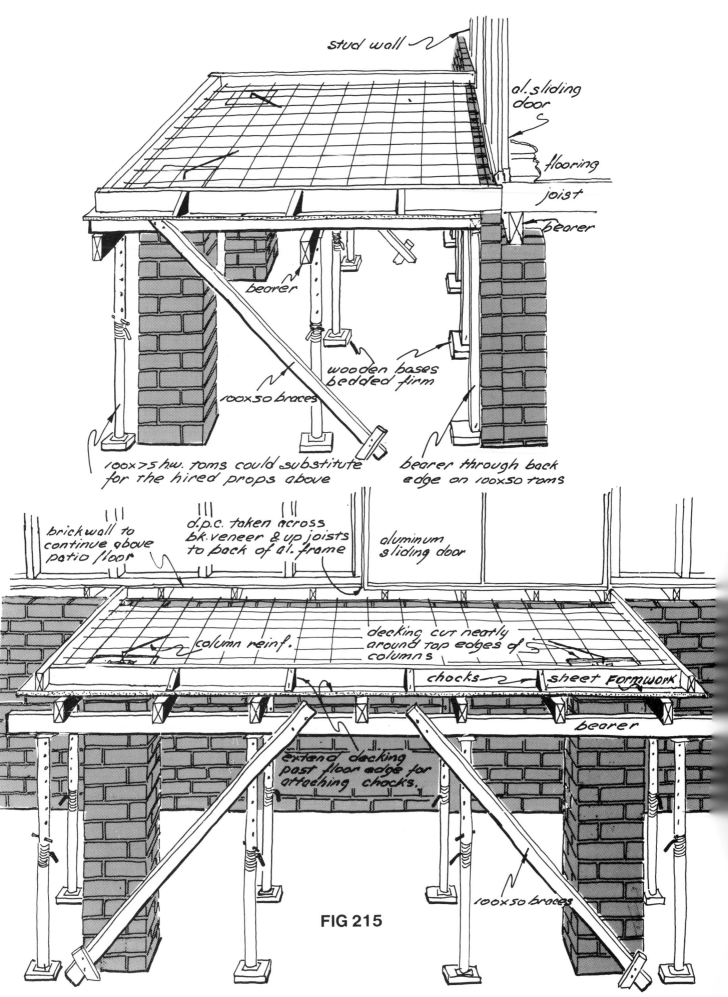

stud wall

al. sliding door

flooring

joist

bearer

bearer

wooden bases bedded firm

100x50 braces

100x75 h.w. toms could substitute for the hired props above

bearer through back edge on 100x50 toms

brick wall to continue above patio floor

d.p.c. taken across bk. veneer & up joists to back of al. frame

aluminum sliding door

column reinf.

decking cut neatly around top edges of columns

chocks

sheet Formwork

bearer

extend decking post floor edge for attaching chocks.

100x50 braces

FIG 215

Bricklaying

Bricklaying Mortar

Correct mortar mix for below DPC and in contact with earth.
1 part cement, ½ part lime, 4½ parts sand

Correct mortar mix for above floor framing level i.e. above the DPC.
1 part cement, 1 part lime, 6 parts sand to which may be added a plasticiser for ease of working. An improved mixture is obtained by using a mechanical mixer. The mortar consistency or its pliability and stickiness is a very important factor to successful bricklaying. A small to medium quantity of mortar on the trowel should be capable of being held upside down without falling off. See page 107. Too wet or too dry a mixture will impair progress considerably.

Laying Bricks

Mortar joints are usually 10mm thick but the wet mortar is laid to about 20mm thick to allow for mortar to be squeezed out when brick is positioned. String lines are attached and pulled taut. Bricks are buttered on one end and laid up against the preceding brick, then tapped down to the string line. Any squeezed out mortar is then removed. Corners are built up to a maximum of 1.2m high and intermediate sections filled in. See figures 216 & 217. This enables mortar joints to set evenly throughout. Jointing is carried out as mortar firms a little. Brush completed brickwork down or use a piece of bagging when sufficiently dry.

Jointing

Although the raked joint is popularly in use, the ironed joint offers superior protection for the clay brick from the elements. Where joints are exposed to salt air, it is preferable to apply the ironed joint method.

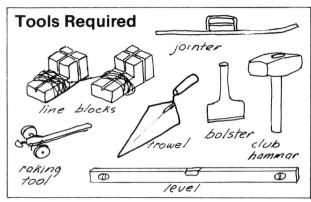

Tools Required

line blocks, jointer, trowel, bolster, club hammer, raking tool, level

How to Construct Brick Walls

One of two methods can be used for levelling and gauging the height of each course. The first one consists of building up raked or stepped corners using a level and a straightedge as in figure 217 and filling in between. The second and more desirable for application by the inexperienced requires the erecting of corner profile posts with nails driven at each course for attaching string lines.

How to Prepare Profile Posts
See figure 216

90mm×45mm straight edged posts are erected at each corner. Bracing them plumb, indicate the first course on all profile posts using a Builders tripod level or water level. Alternatively, simply level off the floor if you are sure it is level. A gauge rod is now made using 50mm x 20mm stock or similar and all brick joint positions indicated on one edge. See fig 217. This rod is held on the profile posts aligning with the first course previously marked and all joint positions transferred across. Nails are driven in these marks to support the string line. This method relieves the bricklayer of all levelling and height measuring while laying bricks and is an excellent method for beginners.

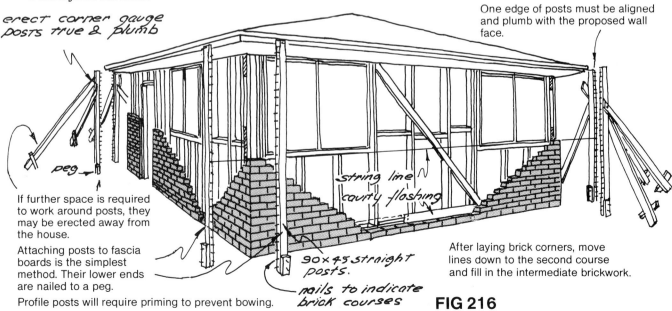

erect corner gauge posts true & plumb

One edge of posts must be aligned and plumb with the proposed wall face.

peg

string line

cavity flashing

If further space is required to work around posts, they may be erected away from the house.

Attaching posts to fascia boards is the simplest method. Their lower ends are nailed to a peg.

Profile posts will require priming to prevent bowing.

90×45 straight posts.

nails to indicate brick courses

After laying brick corners, move lines down to the second course and fill in the intermediate brickwork.

FIG 216

Laying Bricks Using Profile Posts Method

Bricklaying Cont.

Constructing Walls Using Raked Corners

Step 1 Lay one course around the perimeter of proposed brickwork.

Step 2 Construct corners by laying the corner brick first, then the brick at the end of the rake in both walls. Then using the line & blocks, fill in the intermediate bricks. As each course is laid, apply the gauge rod to check height and maintain each course plumb and level. To ensure each raking brick is true, use the straight-edge on the face and edge of the rake.

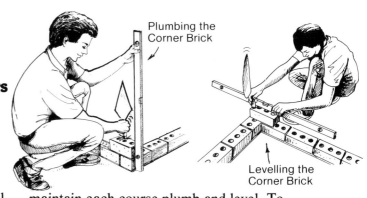

Plumbing the Corner Brick

Levelling the Corner Brick

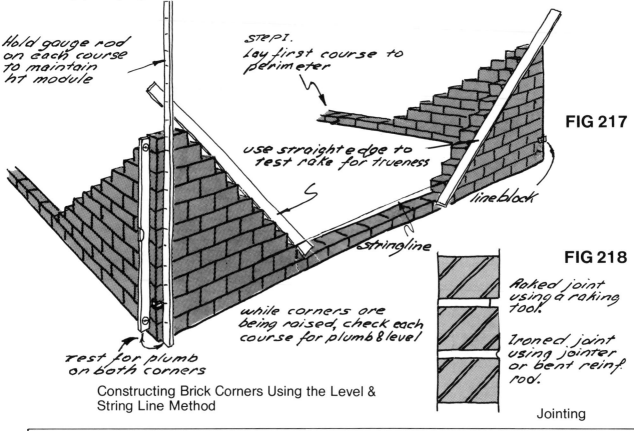

Hold gauge rod on each course to maintain ht module

STEP I. Lay first course to perimeter

use straight edge to test rake for trueness

FIG 217

line block

stringline

while corners are being raised, check each course for plumb & level

Test for plumb on both corners

Constructing Brick Corners Using the Level & String Line Method

FIG 218

Raked joint using a raking tool.

Ironed joint using jointer or bent reinf. rod.

Jointing

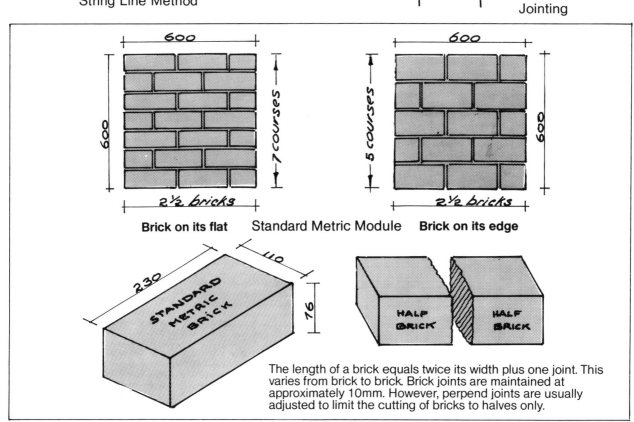

600

600

7 courses

2½ bricks

Brick on its flat   Standard Metric Module   **Brick on its edge**

5 courses

600

2½ bricks

230 110 76

STANDARD METRIC BRICK

HALF BRICK   HALF BRICK

The length of a brick equals twice its width plus one joint. This varies from brick to brick. Brick joints are maintained at approximately 10mm. However, perpend joints are usually adjusted to limit the cutting of bricks to halves only.

How to Lay Bricks

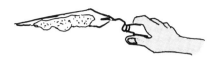

Step 1 Test mortar for correct consistency. See page 105

Step 2 Lay the mortar bed.

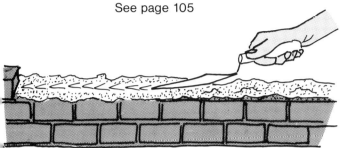

Step 3 Furrow the mortar bed.

Step 4 Salvage the spread mortar from each side of wall.

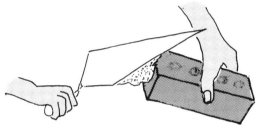

Step 5 While retaining the trowel in one hand, pick up a brick with the other and select the face. Then butter the perpend. Either end of the perpend can be buttered depending in which direction the bricks are being laid.

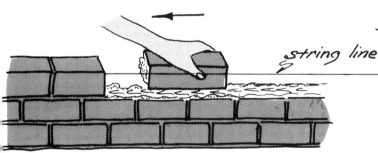

Step 6 Place the brick into the mortar bed and firm down with the hand and fingers and gentle taps with the edge of the trowel.

Note – Bricks can be laid in either direction.

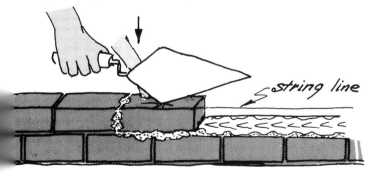

Step 7 Using trowel, tap brick down to the line.

Step 8 Remove mortar that has squeezed out of joint.

Step 9 Jointing should be performed as soon as mortar has firmed sufficiently.

Safety on the Job

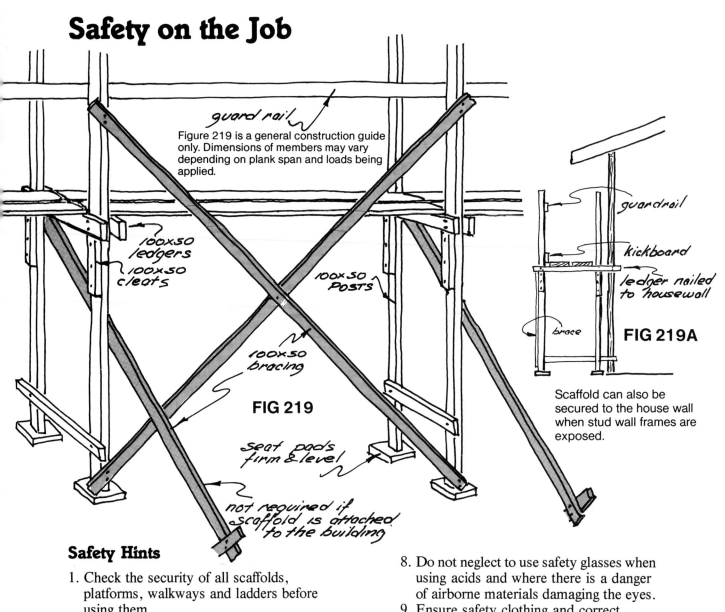

guard rail

Figure 219 is a general construction guide only. Dimensions of members may vary depending on plank span and loads being applied.

100x50 ledgers

100x50 cleats

100x50 posts

100x50 bracing

FIG 219

seat pads firm & level

not required if scaffold is attached to the building

guardrail

kickboard

ledger nailed to housewall

brace

FIG 219A

Scaffold can also be secured to the house wall when stud wall frames are exposed.

Safety Hints

1. Check the security of all scaffolds, platforms, walkways and ladders before using them.
2. Always check that persons or electrical cables are not underneath before throwing down materials or tools from elevated positions.
3. Lock up dangerous objects before leaving the site.

8. Do not neglect to use safety glasses when using acids and where there is a danger of airborne materials damaging the eyes.
9. Ensure safety clothing and correct breathing apparatus is worn when using asbestos.
   Inhaled asbestos fibres can cause Asbestosis and a variety of life threatening cancers.

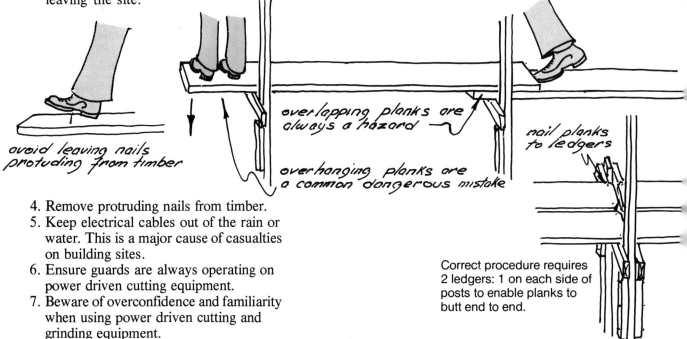

avoid leaving nails protuding from timber

overlapping planks are always a hazard

overhanging planks are a common dangerous mistake

nail planks to ledgers

4. Remove protruding nails from timber.
5. Keep electrical cables out of the rain or water. This is a major cause of casualties on building sites.
6. Ensure guards are always operating on power driven cutting equipment.
7. Beware of overconfidence and familiarity when using power driven cutting and grinding equipment.

Correct procedure requires 2 ledgers: 1 on each side of posts to enable planks to butt end to end.

Carport Plan

Note: Council approval must be obtained to construct a carport.

How to Construct a Carport

Step 1 Establish position of carport and erect profile corners as on Page 23. Set out on profiles all post positions.

Step 2 Two methods are common for supporting beams. The first is to erect and brace temporary posts of 100 x 50mm to support the two side beams.

Establish beams level and complete the roof. Then dig the holes. Working on sawstools, attach the gal. M.S. post stirrups to the permanent posts.
Fix posts to beam with stirrups suspended in holes.

Pour concrete and plumb posts while concrete is setting.

The other method is to dig holes first, pour concrete and insert post stirrups adjusting them into alignment to a string line. Then after a day or so, attach posts plumb and temporarily brace. Some high wind areas may require the rafters to be strapped to the beams. Wall bracing is applied to the end and one side as indicated by the dotted lines.

Bracing

Although wood compression braces have been illustrated steel braces could be applied. Check with a local Plan Designer or Engineer to obtain the correct sectional size.
The wood braces should be bolted or strapped each end to the adjoining members.

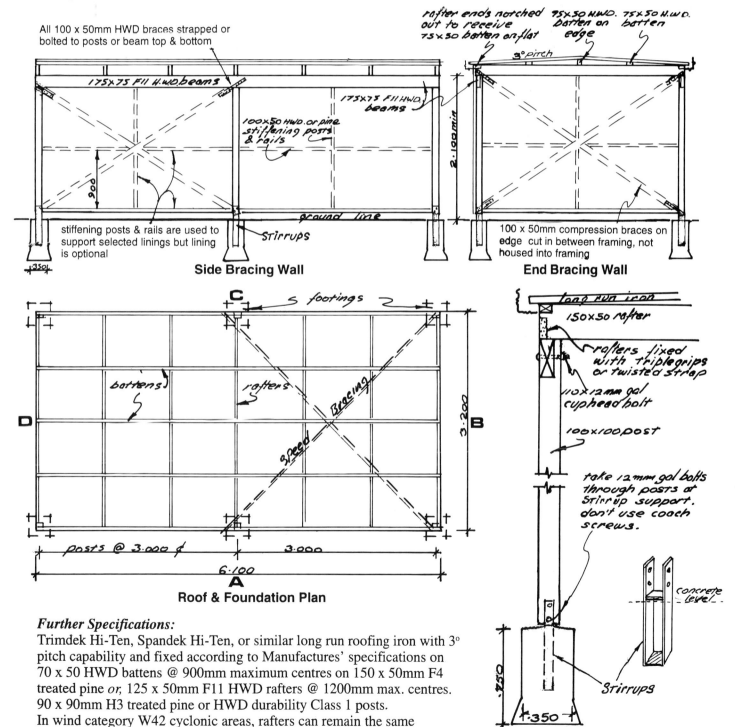

Side Bracing Wall

End Bracing Wall

Roof & Foundation Plan

Post & Footing Detail

Further Specifications:

Trimdek Hi-Ten, Spandek Hi-Ten, or similar long run roofing iron with 3° pitch capability and fixed according to Manufactures' specifications on 70 x 50 HWD battens @ 900mm maximum centres on 150 x 50mm F4 treated pine *or,* 125 x 50mm F11 HWD rafters @ 1200mm max. centres. 90 x 90mm H3 treated pine or HWD durability Class 1 posts.
In wind category W42 cyclonic areas, rafters can remain the same dimensions but the spacings must be reduced to 900mm max. centres.

Fireplace & Chimneys

Brick Fireplaces & Chimneys

Construction of fireplaces and chimneys should be carried out by a bricklayer who has had previous experience. Plans should give all dimensions of footings, fireplace opening, throat, flue and chimney etc.

Important

The 2 major faults that can occur with fireplaces are:-
a. Faulty smoke drawing capability.
b. Water penetration down the chimney during rain.
It is important that a tried and proven formula be used to establish proportions and to ensure against faulty smoke drawing.
To prevent water penetration the following features should be included:-

1. A copper tray installed through chimney at the roof height with edges folded up on the inside of the flue and weep holes positioned at this level.

2. Chimneys topped with a cap and side openings are preferred. These should be positioned on the sides away from prevailing winds.

3. Flashings fitted correctly at roof level.

Important Pointers

A. Ensure waterproof fire mortar and fire bricks are used in fireplace back, back hearth, floor and throat.

B. All timber framing members to be kept 50mm away from brick structure. It is good practice to line the face of trimming timbers surrounding the chimney with asbestos cement sheeting or a fireproof material.

C. Use a brick tie at each brick at roof framing level.

D. If fireplaces are situated on a wall, it is preferable to position them as centrally as possible rather than at the end of a long narrow room.
The fireplace should not be located beside doorways or where draughts could interfere with the smoke flow.

E. All fireplaces should have a safety screen surrounding the opening to contain flying sparks.

F. The hearth must be entirely supported by the chimney. It is cantilevered as on elevation B.B. and must not be joined to the house structure.

G. A clear space must be maintained between the sloping fireplace back and the brick rear wall and filled with dry shingle or fine broken bricks.

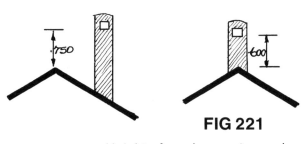

FIG 221

Height of smoke apertures above roofs

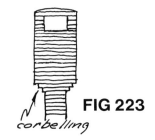

FIG 223

corbelling

Corbelling can be carried out in the ceiling space or above the roof.

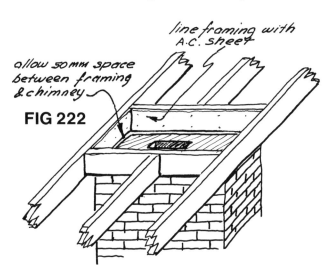

allow 50mm space between framing & chimney

line framing with A.C. sheet

FIG 222

Framing around chimneys

Steps of Construction

Step 1 Foundations are poured.

Step 2 Brickwork brought up to floor level.

Step 3 Timber floor, wall framing and roof erected with timbers being trimmed ready for chimney to pass through.

Step 4 fireplace and chimney erected and flashings fitted.

Step 5 Roofing laid and flashings permanently bedded.

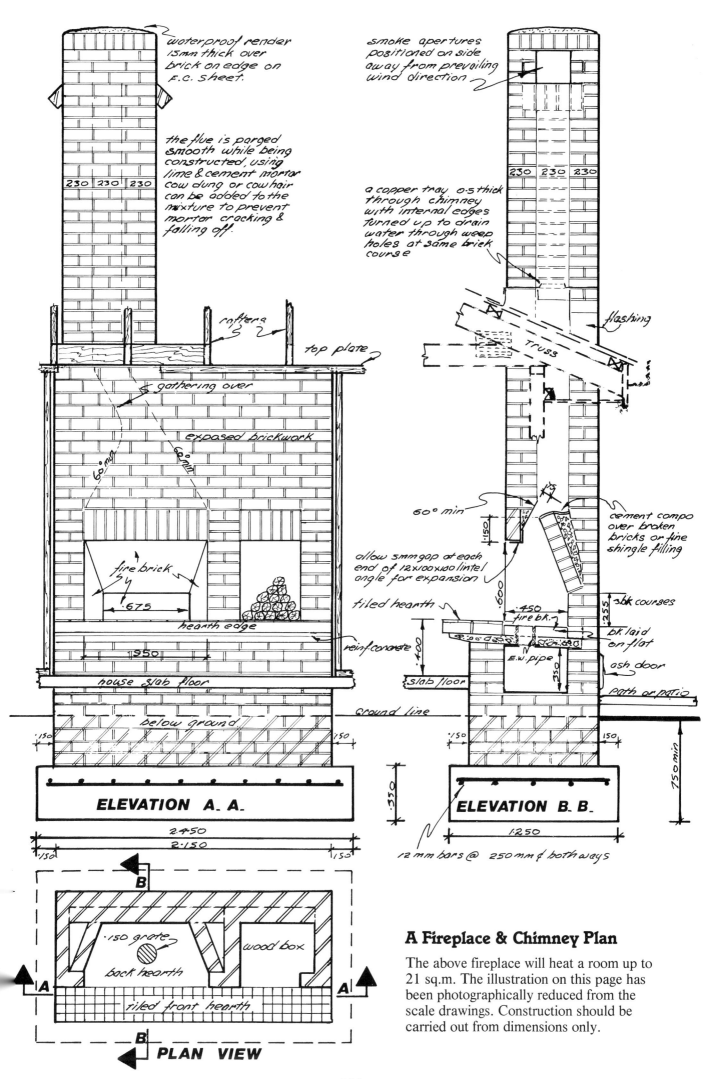

waterproof render 15mm thick over brick on edge on f.c. sheet.

smoke apertures positioned on side away from prevailing wind direction

the flue is parged smooth while being constructed, using lime & cement mortar cow dung or cow hair can be added to the mixture to prevent mortar cracking & falling off.

a copper tray 0.5 thick through chimney with internal edges turned up to drain water through weep holes at same brick course

230 230 230

230 230 230

flashing

rafters

top plate

Truss

gathering over

exposed brickwork

60° min

60° min

60° min

cement compo over broken bricks or fine shingle filling

fire brick

allow 5mm gap at each end of 12×100×100 lintel angle for expansion

·150

·600

·450 fire bk.

·675

tiled hearth

·255 3 bk courses

hearth edge

reinf. concrete

·550

·400

E.W. pipe

·250

bk. laid on flat

ash door

house slab floor

slab floor

path or patio

Ground line

below ground

·150

·150

·150

·150

ELEVATION A. A.

ELEVATION B. B.

·350

750 min

2·450

2·150

·150

·150

1·250

12 mm bars @ 250 mm ∅ both ways

B

A

·150 grate

wood box

back hearth

A

tiled front hearth

B

PLAN VIEW

A Fireplace & Chimney Plan

The above fireplace will heat a room up to 21 sq.m. The illustration on this page has been photographically reduced from the scale drawings. Construction should be carried out from dimensions only.

Index

Note: Italic numbers are cross references to pages in **How to be a Successful Owner Builder and Renovator.**